THE INCREDIBLE Book of Mad MAZES

ANDY PETERS

Sandy Creek
NEW YORK

Sandy Creek
NEW YORK

An Imprint of Sterling Publishing
387 Park Avenue South
New York, NY 10016

ISBN 978-1-4351-5929-7

Mazes designed and illustrated by Andy Peters
Written by Joe Fullman, Patience Coster, and Samantha Noonan
Edited by Kate Overy
Designed by Linday Storey and Tokiko Morishima

Manufactured in China
Lot #:
2 4 6 8 10 9 7 5 3 1
01/15

CONTENTS

Help Max, Millie, and Mojo the dog find their way through the mad mazes of these three awesome adventures. First up is a fun-packed trip around the world. Next comes a thrilling journey through Space before the gang climbs aboard a time machine for a trip through the ages. It's going to be a-mazing!

Look out for Ted the ginger cat. He tags along with the gang and pops up in every maze!

MAZES AROUND THE WORLD

CONTENTS

Chapter 1
ON TOP OF THE WORLD

Ready for the trip of a lifetime? Join, Max, Millie, and Mojo the dog on the ultimate tour around the globe. Help the gang solve the mazes and be sure to look out for Ted, the ginger cat who pops up in every location. Their journey starts at the top of the world in the frozen Arctic.

Northern Lights

Ski with Millie, Max, and Mojo through the Norwegian wood to the log cabin.

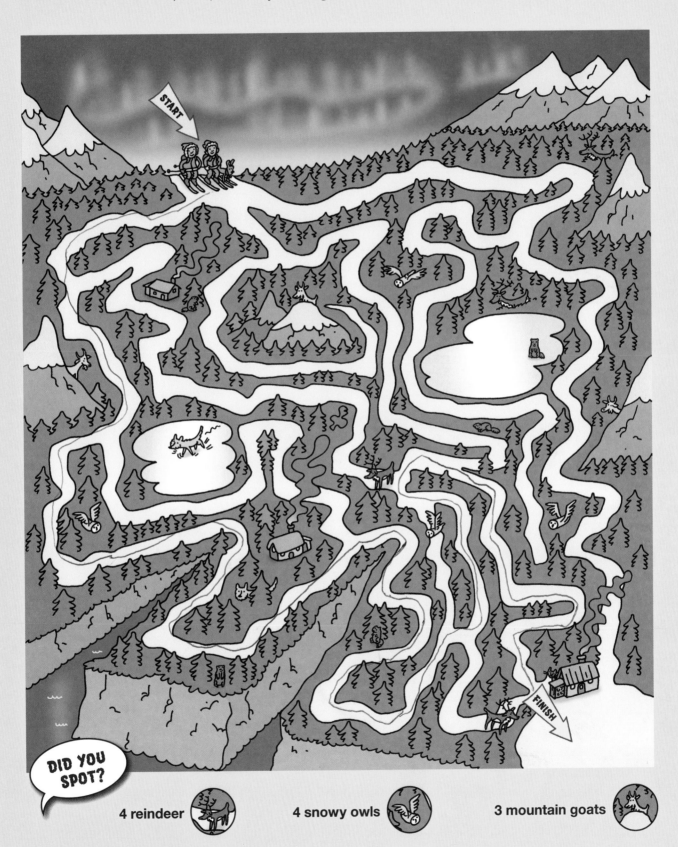

DID YOU SPOT?

4 reindeer   **4 snowy owls**   **3 mountain goats**

Going on a Bear Hunt!

Find out where the polar bear is hiding.

DID YOU SPOT?

2 happy hares   4 snow geese   The sly Arctic fox

Iceberg!

Help steer the ship through the icebergs and patches of pack ice.

DID YOU SPOT?

5 hiding huskies   6 slippery seals   The polar bear

Husky Chase

Guide your team of huskies past the igloos to the finish.

DID YOU SPOT?

20 lost Christmas presents   **4 seals**   **The nosey narwhal**

Moscow March

Step lively in Russia along the route of this Red Square maze.

Glacier Tour

Crunch your way across this glacier to the ocean.

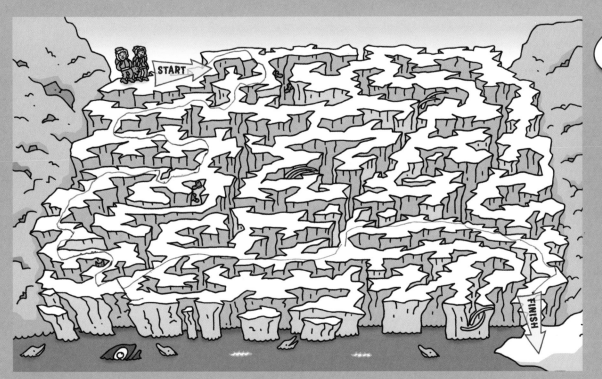

11

Fire and Ice

Make your way through the erupting volcanoes of Iceland to the finish.

A Date With Dracula

Help our heroes escape from the Count's creepy castle.

Chapter 2
CiTY HOPPiNG

Help Millie, Max, and Mojo weave their way through a world of maze-filled cities. Look out for Ted the cat everywhere you go!

Venetian Tiles

Pick a pathway across this square in Venice, Italy. No stepping on the lines!

FINISH

START

DID YOU SPOT?

The gondolier

The bowl of pasta

The purple pigeon

Clues in the Zoo

In Germany, follow the path past the animals in Berlin Zoo to the finish.

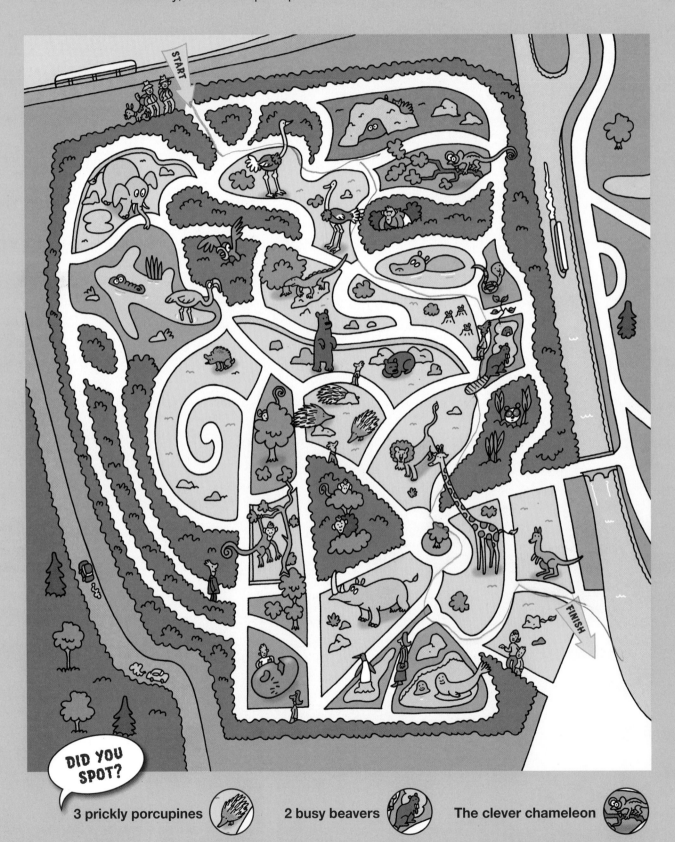

START

FINISH

DID YOU SPOT?

3 prickly porcupines

2 busy beavers

The clever chameleon

16

Chinese Pagoda

Find your way out of this tower in Wuhan City, China.

DID YOU SPOT?

The bird with a hat on

The tourist in the green hat

Gladiator!

Find a route out of this action-packed Roman colosseum!

DID YOU SPOT?

5 Roman coins

The scary blue monster

Lady of New York

Climb down the Statue of Liberty in New York City, without crossing the lines.

Prisoners in the Tower

Can you find the way to the middle of the Tower of London in England?

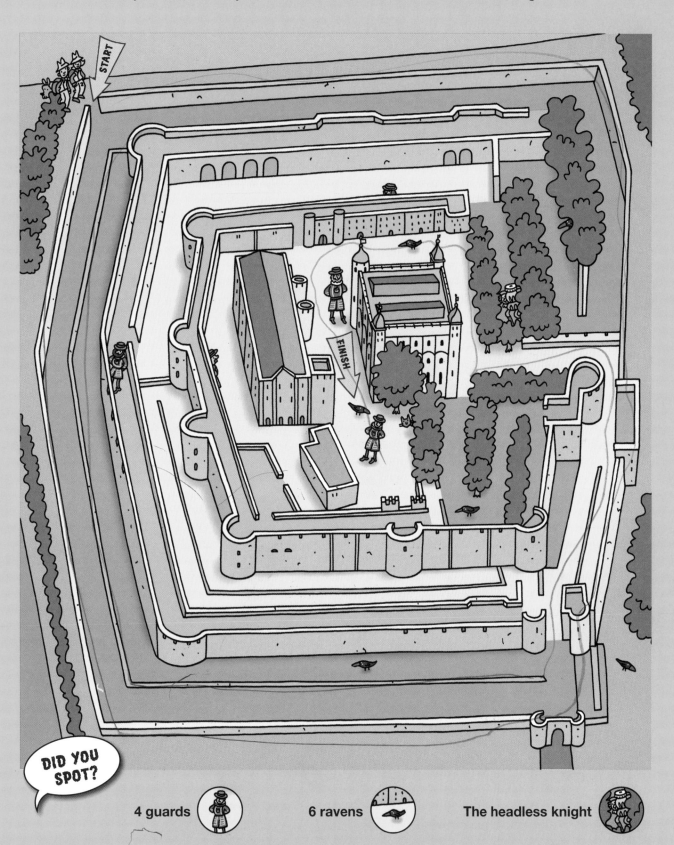

DID YOU SPOT?

4 guards   **6 ravens**   **The headless knight**

Eiffely High!

Scramble down the ironwork of the Eiffel Tower in Paris, France.

Acropolis

Find the route through this ancient settlement in Athens, Greece.

DID YOU SPOT?

5 Grecian urns   3 gray sacred cats   The Trojan horse

Chapter 3
OCEAN VOYAGE

The friends are off to explore the ocean blue. Help them find their way through a world of watery wonders, pirate attacks, and deep discoveries!

Leaving the Docks

Help Max, Millie, and Mojo find their way to the ship through the busy port.

DID YOU SPOT?

The blue truck   The worker in a white helmet   The bird on the pulley

Shipping Lanes

Navigate these busy shipping highways.

DID YOU SPOT?

The purple buoy

The yellow flag

Sargasso Sea

Find your way through this smelly, seaweedy ocean!

DID YOU SPOT?

3 turtles

5 plastic bottles

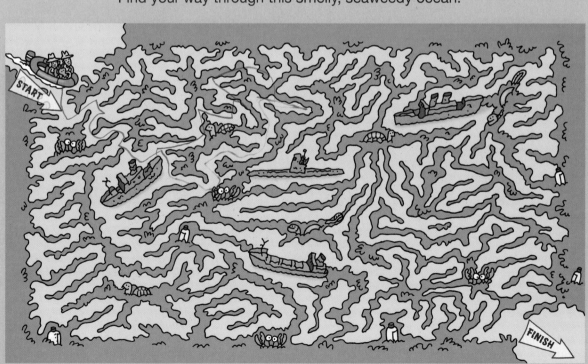

The Devil's Triangle

Help our heroes steer a course through the whirlpools of the Bermuda Triangle.

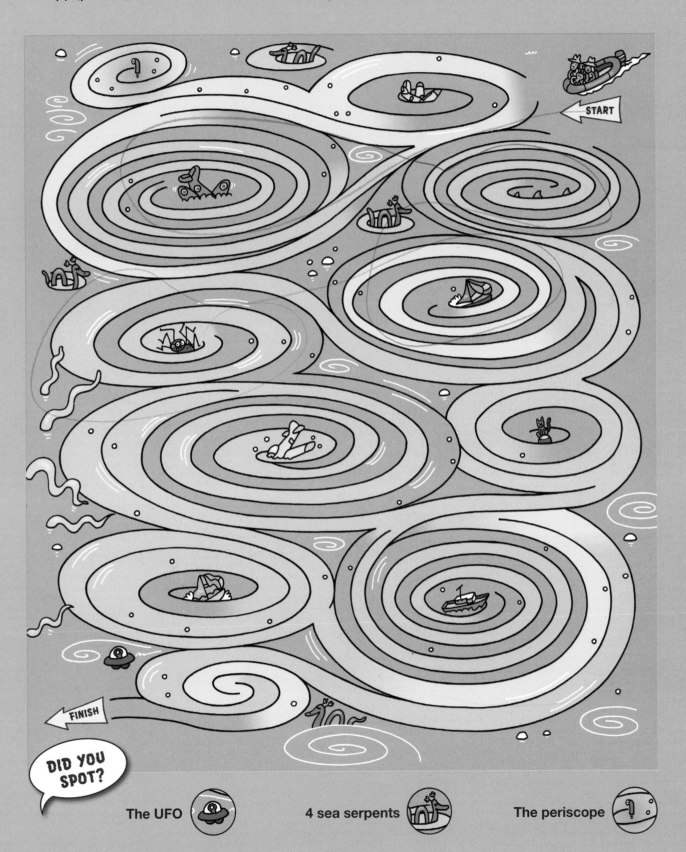

START

FINISH

DID YOU SPOT?

The UFO   4 sea serpents   The periscope

Cabin Fever

Can you creep up on deck without waking the pirates?

Battle the High Seas

Shiver me timbers! Can you navigate your way through the whirling waters,
avoid the giant octopus, and wink at the whales before escaping to safety at the finish?

DID YOU SPOT?

The moaning mermaid   **The pirate treasure**   **The pink crab**

Shipwrecked!

Max, Millie, and Mojo have washed up on a tropical island.
Help them find their way to the treasure chest.

DID YOU SPOT?

3 hummingbirds   2 pirate hats   The skeleton

Kidnapped!

The pirates have trapped Max, Millie, and Mojo in their den! Help our heroes escape from Skull Cove.

DID YOU SPOT?

4 pesky pirates   3 treasure chests   14 barrels of rum

Chapter 4
THE WILD WEST

Yee-haw! Saddle up and ride through the open prairies and mountains of North America. See how many alligators, bears, and coyotes you can spot!

Niagara

Help Max, Millie, and Mojo meet this whitewater rafting challenge over Niagara Falls.

DID YOU SPOT?

4 purple fish   3 happy ducks   The baby bear

Dinosaur Dig

Help the fossil hunters pick a path through the prehistoric bones.

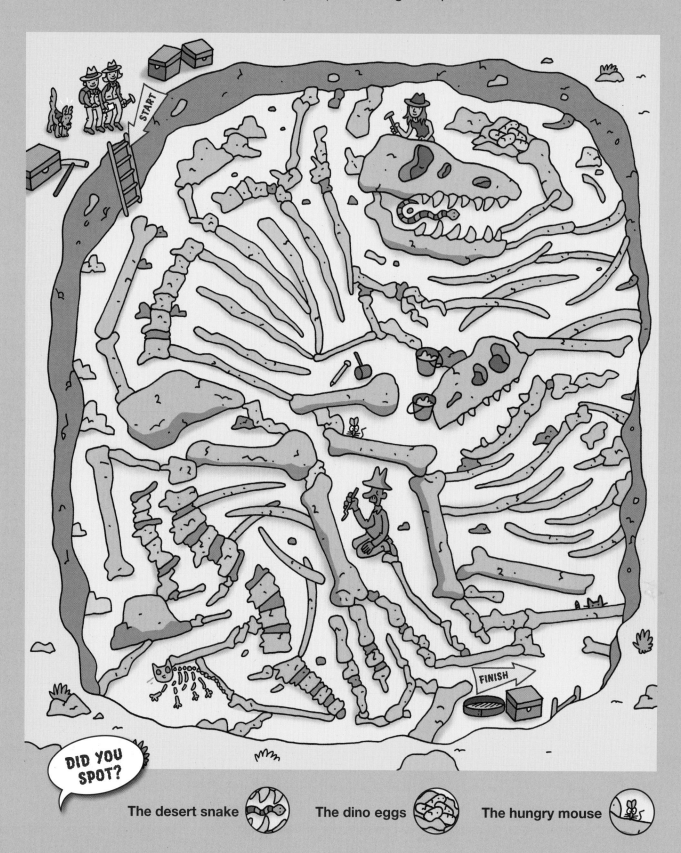

START

FINISH

DID YOU SPOT?

The desert snake   **The dino eggs**   **The hungry mouse**

Cherokee Trail

Choose the right track to take you to the end of the trail.
Watch out for hungry bears, deadly snakes, and poison ivy!

DID YOU SPOT?

3 grizzly bears   3 giant mosquitoes   The secret railroad

Swamped!

Float along until you find a turn that takes you out of the Florida Everglades.

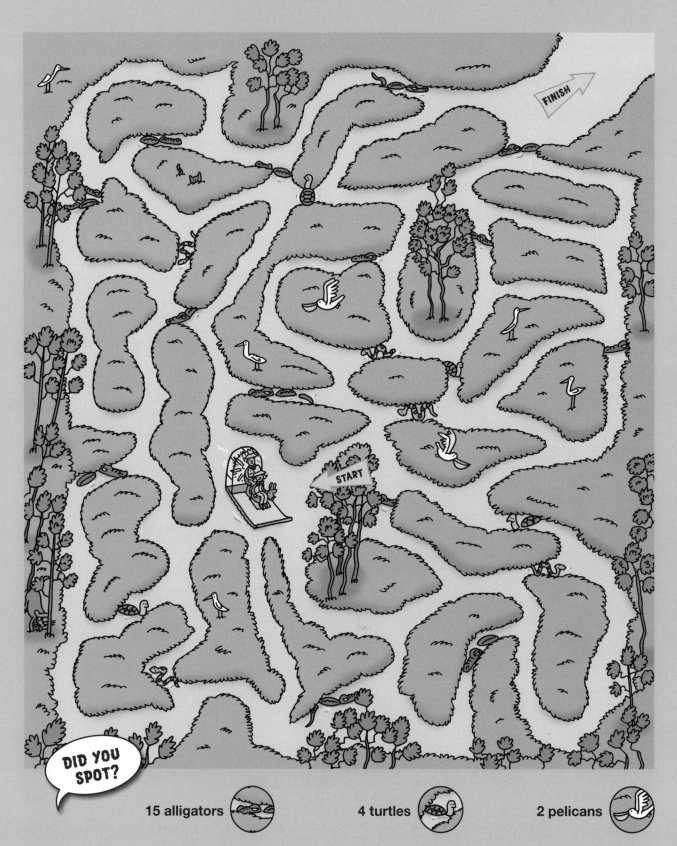

15 alligators   4 turtles   2 pelicans

Tornado!

It's a twister – and you're inside! Find a way to get your feet back on the ground.

DID YOU SPOT?

3 scared cows   The blue car   The lost bike

Cattle Drive

Find a way through the herd on this cowboy cattle drive across the country.

Medicine Wheel

Find the route through this Native American medicine wheel.

Mount Rushmore

Climb down this famous monument of four American presidents.

DID YOU SPOT?

3 bald eagles

5 brown rabbits

Yellowstone Park

Take a trip through this national park – but watch out for the bears!

DID YOU SPOT?

4 moose

The cheeky rabbit

38

Rocky Road

Explore the Grand Canyon and find a way through the desert landscape.

Chapter 5
iNCAS AND OTHERS

Help Max, Millie, and Mojo unlock the secrets of Latin America. Explore the mysterious Cave of the Hands, visit the floating islands on Lake Titicaca, and look for a blue-footed booby in the Galapagos!

Mexican Temple

Find your way from the top to the bottom of this ancient Mayan building in Mexico.

DID YOU SPOT?

5 cheeky monkeys

2 toucans

The jungle spirit

Carnival!

Get into the spirit of the Rio carnival in Brazil as you guide Max, Millie, and Mojo through the maze of samba dancers.

DID YOU SPOT?

The fire-eater   3 tambourines   4 trumpets

Rainforest Ramble

Paddle your canoe to the starting point of this jungle maze, then fight your way through Brazil's Amazon rainforest to the finish.

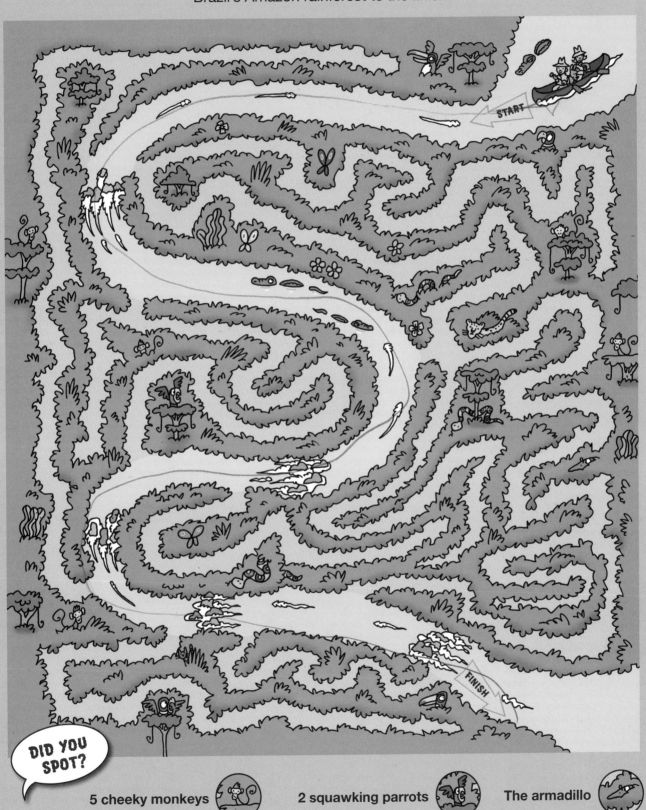

DID YOU SPOT?

5 cheeky monkeys   2 squawking parrots   The armadillo

Sinkhole City

Find your way across town, avoiding the giant potholes!

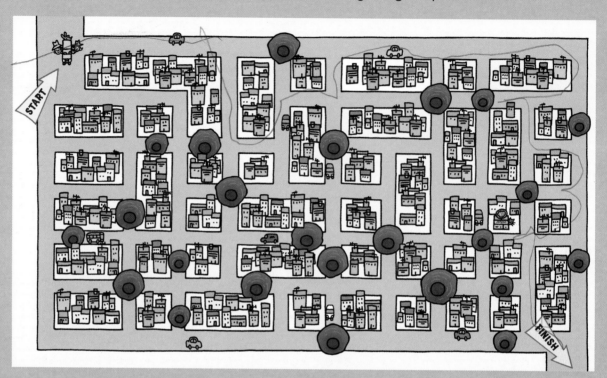

Island Folk

Find a route through the floating reed islands on Lake Titicaca in Bolivia.

44

High in the Andes

Navigate the ruins of this mountain Inca settlement in Peru.

DID YOU SPOT?

3 condors   4 llamas   The ancient crown

Save the Animals!

Find your way through this Galapagos Islands maze. Be careful not to scare the animals away – this is the only place on Earth they can be found!

DID YOU SPOT?

The giant tortoise   The land iguana   The blue-footed booby

Strange Signs

Weave your way through the mysterious Nazca lines in the Peruvian desert.

Cave of the Hands

Got your flashlight handy? Feel your way through these
underground caves to emerge up onto the surface of Argentina.

DID YOU SPOT?

2 sets of handprints   **The vampire bat**   **The scary monster**

Salty Scramble

Make your way across these salt flats in Chile, keeping clear of the prickly cacti!

Chapter 6
Go EXPLORE!

Cross Africa in a jeep, surf in the desert, and climb a giant tree in Zanzibar. Travel east to track the yeti to its lair and dance with dragons in China!

On Safari

Steer a path through the animals on Tanzania's Serengeti Plains.

DID YOU SPOT?

4 wary warthogs   3 shy snakes   3 enormous elephants

Watering Hole

Make your way through the animal bathtime!

DID YOU SPOT?

6 wallowing warthogs   5 cunning crocs   The swimming snake

Gorilla Mountain

Find your way through the Rwandan mountains, avoiding the sleeping gorillas.

START

FINISH

DID YOU SPOT?

2 okapis   Gerald the giraffe   The sleepiest gorilla

Riding the Dunes

Surf down the dunes in the Sahara Desert.

DID YOU SPOT?

4 geckos

2 jackals

The Big Tree

Climb down through the branches of this giant tree in Zanzibar.

DID YOU SPOT?

The red monkey

The mongoose

Abominable Snowman

Help Max, Millie, and Mojo as they track the yeti down the mountain to his secret hideout in the Himalayas!

DID YOU SPOT?

The werewolf

A pair of yeti slippers

The unicorn

Angkor Wat

Help the friends find their way out of this temple in Cambodia.

Secret Tunnels

Find your way to ground level through these tunnels in Vietnam.

Stone Forest

Plot your rocky route to the pagoda through this Chinese landscape.

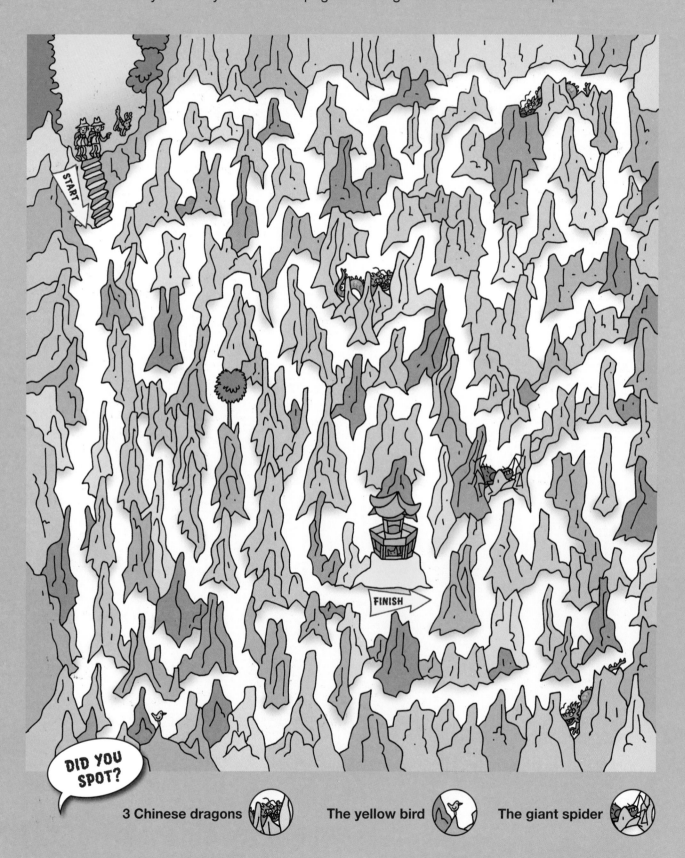

Dragon Dance

Find your way through this maze of Chinese dragons.

DID YOU SPOT?

The dragon with blue eyes

The dragon breathing fire

The dragon who has lost its fire

59

Chapter 7
DOWN UNDER

Explore the Australian outback and New Zealand wilderness. Here you can zip line through the forest, bungee jump off a tower, scale a rock face, and take a helicopter ride through a fireworks display!

Hopalong!

Bounce your way around Australia's Kangaroo Island!

DID YOU SPOT?

4 sneaky sharks   5 cool koalas   4 pleased pelicans

Catch the Wave!

Speed through the surf at the famous Bondi Beach in Sydney.

Walkabout

Can you survive the scorching Australian outback?
Make your way past the Bungle Bungles and around Uluru (Ayers Rock).

DID YOU SPOT?

4 snakes

5 wombats

2 wallabies

A Fishy Puzzle

Wiggle your way through this aboriginal dot painting.

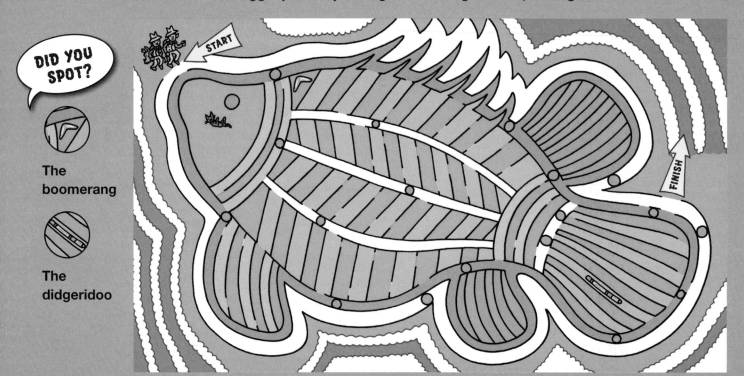

Umbrella Beach

Steer a path through the sunbathers and beach parasols.

Musical Landmark

Burst into song as you guide Max, Millie, and Mojo down from the roof of the Sydney Opera House.

Ropes and Zips

Climb across the rope bridges and swing on the zip lines in this wilderness adventure in Tasmania.

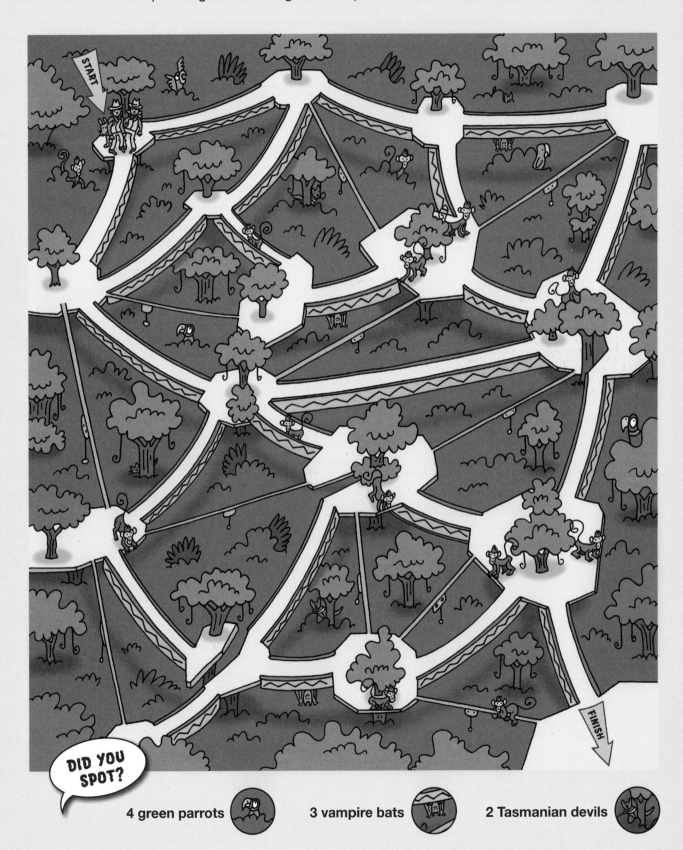

Sky Tower

Make your way through the bungee jumpers on this New Zealand tower in Auckland.

START

FINISH

DID YOU SPOT?

The giant spider   The shy gorilla   The superhero

The Great Wall

Can you get past the armed guard on the Great Wall of China?

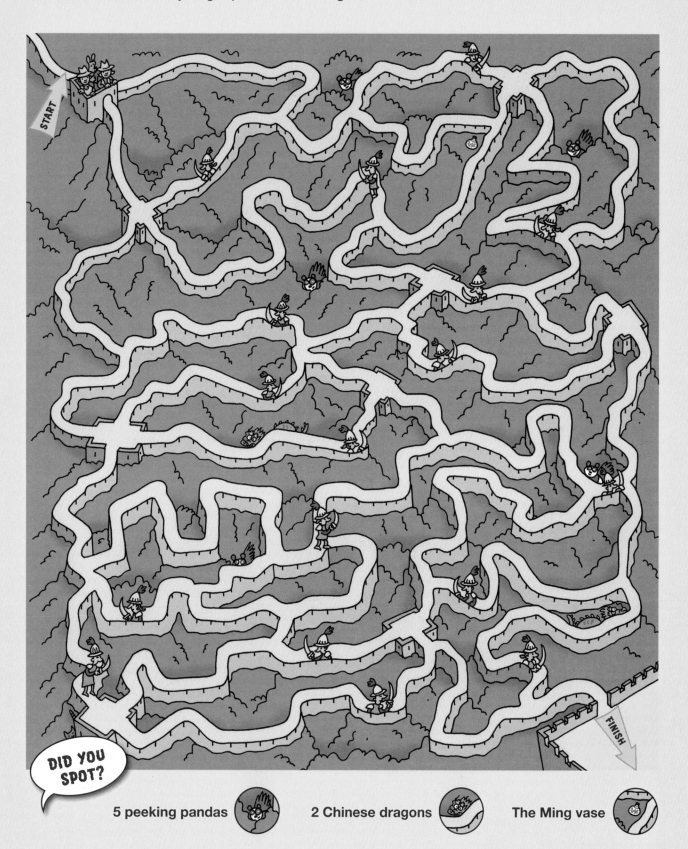

START

FINISH

DID YOU SPOT?

5 peeking pandas   2 Chinese dragons   The Ming vase

Terracotta Army

Weave your way through the Chinese clay warriors.

DID YOU SPOT?

The one-armed soldier

The ceremonial sword

Mojo's New Look

Mojo has been built in stone! Puzzle your way down the doggie sphinx in Egypt.

DID YOU SPOT?

3 stinging scorpions

2 chatting camels

Pyramid

Phew – it's a scorcher today! Can you walk like an Egyptian and find your way to the top of the perilous pyramid? Then you can dive into the lovely cool water.

DID YOU SPOT?

The desert dog   **The mischievous mouse**   **The slithering snake**

Rice Terraces

Climb from the top to the bottom of these terraces in the Philippines.

Amazing Islands

Can you steer a route through these manmade islands in Dubai?

DID YOU SPOT?

The star island

3 crazy crabs

2 sand bunnies

Up, Up, and Away

Help the friends to safety in the hot-air balloon basket.

Home at Last!

Help each of the friends to find their bedrooms for a well-earned rest.

DID YOU SPOT?

The snazzy skateboard   The rubber duck   The roving rabbit

MAZES
ACROSS THE
UNIVERSE

CONTENTS

Chapter 1
OUT OF THIS WORLD!

Remember to look out for Ted the cat. He pops up in every maze!

Having recovered from their around-the-world trip, Max, Millie, and Mojo have decided to go camping in the country for a few nights. All is quiet and still, but the weirdest things can happen when you least expect them…

Follow That Star!

The gang is relaxing under the stars and spotting constellations.
Can you find your way to the single, bright star?

Mystery Craft

At dawn, the gang is awakened by a fleet of flying saucers!
Can you direct this bright spaceship to the landing spot?

80

DID YOU SPOT?

3 early birds   A flying cup and saucer   Drying underpants

Come and Join Us!

An alien has asked Max, Millie, and Mojo to join him and his crew
on a very urgent mission. Find your way up the ramp and onto the ship.

DID YOU SPOT?

3 bewildered bears   **The alien captain**   **The alien dog**

Mojo's Dash

Mojo really wants to go on a space adventure with his friends, but he's left his lucky bone behind! Help him rush back to get it before the spaceship takes off.

DID YOU SPOT?

3 men in black

The sneaky photographer

Ginger Cat Stowaway

Ginger Cat has slipped onto the spaceship too! But he needs to hide away. Help him find a dark corner in the engine room.

DID YOU SPOT?

The alien mouse

The mug of toxic tea

Space Invaders

The aliens tell Max, Millie, and Mojo to come up to the control room of the spaceship to collect their space suits.

DID YOU SPOT?

The space spider   **The galactic goldfish**   **The teddy bear**

Up Through The Atmosphere

It's time to go, but the ship has to take off during a meteor shower!
Help steer the spaceship through the meteors and other obstacles.

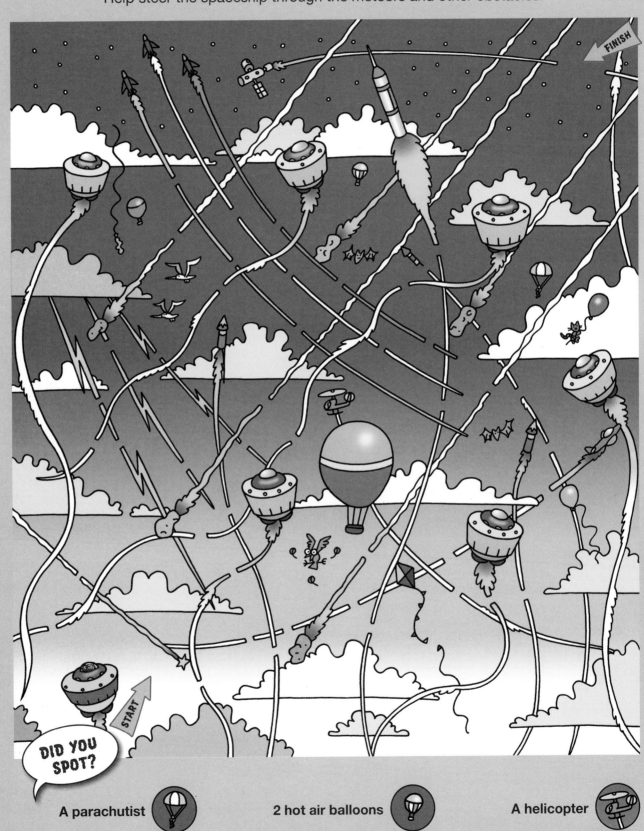

A parachutist

2 hot air balloons

A helicopter

Moon Walk

Max, Millie, and Mojo ask if they can take a walk on the moon.
They are very excited to look back at Earth!

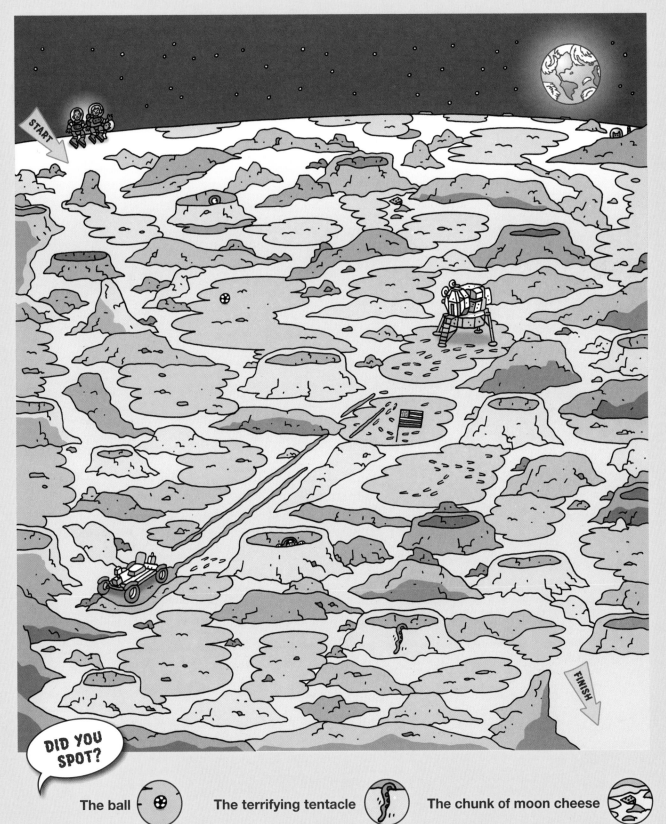

DID YOU SPOT?

The ball   The terrifying tentacle   The chunk of moon cheese

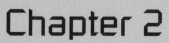

Chapter 2

PERPLEXING PLANETS

The aliens explain that the Mother Star, which powers all the other stars in the Universe, has been broken apart and the pieces stolen. Without it, all the other stars will die. The aliens have been hunting down all the star pieces and now they just have five left to find.

The Sun

The aliens lend the trio a little space shuttle for searching the planets.
Guide it low to the surface of the Sun so they can look for a star piece.

The toasted
marshmallow

A pair of
sunglasses

3 sun salamanders

Magnetic Mercury

Next stop, Mercury! Help the friends fly through the
magnetic field and all the metal objects that it is dragging in.

DID YOU
SPOT?

The tin robot   **The teaspoon**   **The tank**

Metal Men

The metal men of Mercury have gathered to say hello to the gang, but they have no time to stop! Help them get back to the spaceship.

DID YOU SPOT?

4 lost oil cans   3 loose screws   A remote control

Hot Spot

Max, Millie, and Mojo have arrived on Venus! Help them find a way around the lava.

Dragon City

The Venusians aren't as friendly as the metal men on Mercury!
Help the gang get through this scary city quickly.

The baby dragon   The ruby collar   The traffic lights

Star Map

The aliens have asked Max, Millie, and Mojo to navigate the way to Mars.
Can you see on the star map which route they should take?

DID YOU SPOT?

A blue star

4 green stars

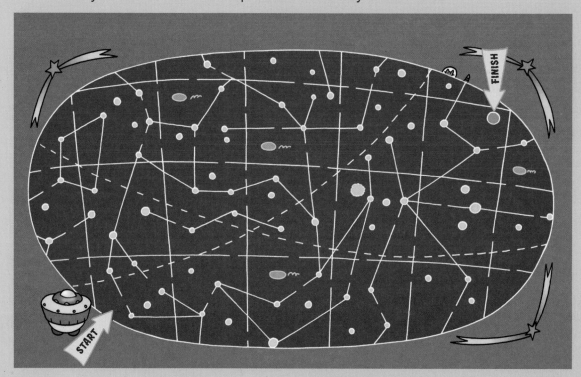

Mojo Lost!

Mojo was having fun exploring the ship, but now he's
lost in the alien canteen! Help him find his way out.

DID YOU SPOT?

The alien pizza

3 empty plates

The Red Planet

Max, Millie, and Mojo have made it to Mars!
Now they need to search the surface for star pieces.

Life on Mars

The aliens decide to stop overnight on Mars, so Max, Millie, and Mojo get to stay with a Martian family. Help them find their bedroom.

DID YOU SPOT?

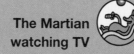

The Martian cat

The Martian watching TV

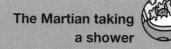

The Martian taking a shower

Alien School Time

The friends search everywhere on Mars for star pieces – even in the school!

START

FINISH

DID YOU SPOT?

The alien fly   The alien hamster   The pink star piece

Chapter 3
DEEP SPACE

The aliens are very grateful to Max, Millie, and Mojo for finding the first star piece (did you spot it?) and want to fly on to find more. Join the friends as they venture into deep space.

Asteroid Belt

Before they can reach any more planets, our crew needs to navigate the famous Asteroid Belt – can you get them out in one piece?

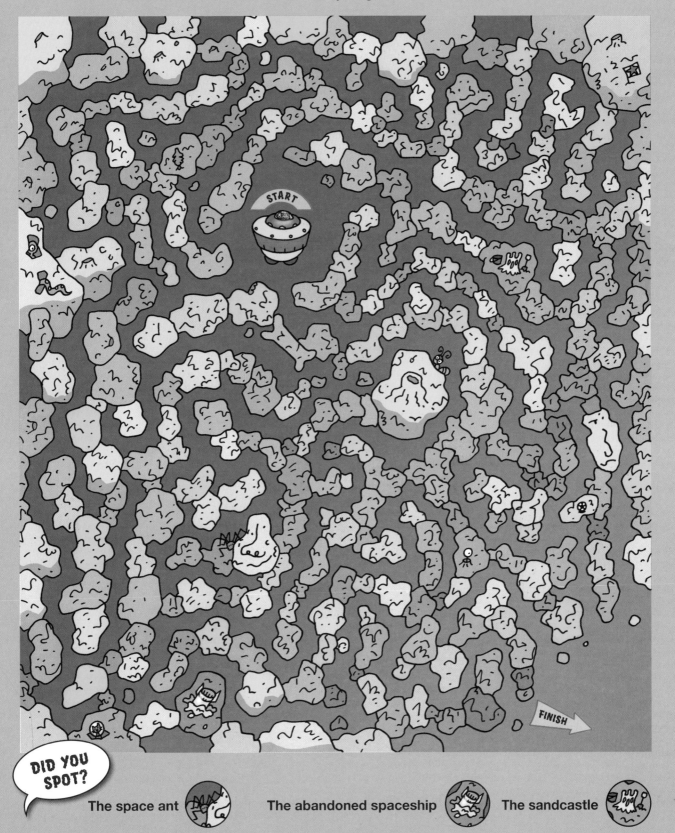

DID YOU SPOT?

The space ant   The abandoned spaceship   The sandcastle

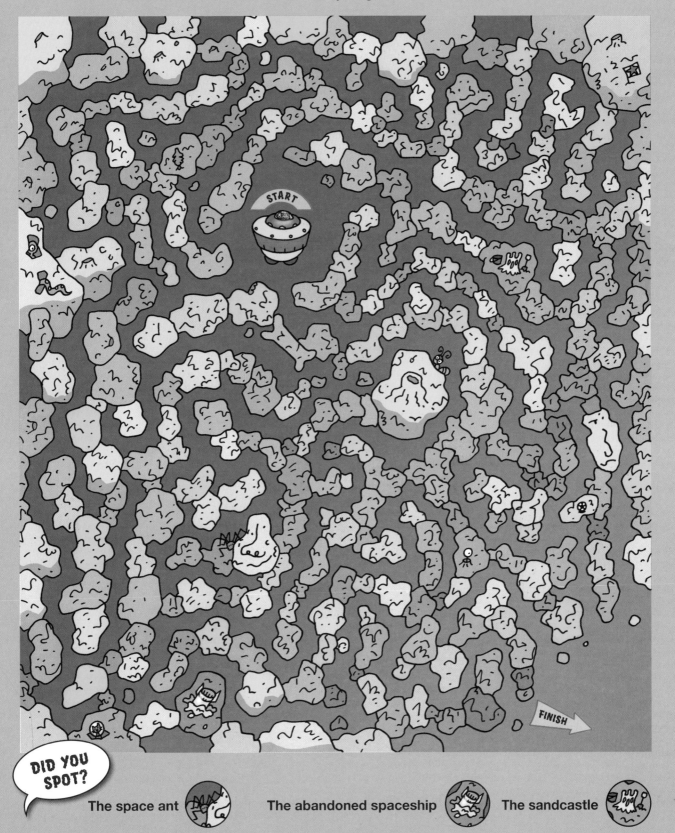

97

The Eye of Jupiter

Is there a star piece swirling in the giant storms on Jupiter?
Help Max, Millie, and Mojo through the maze.

The alien with 3 arms   The balloon   The kite

Many Moons

Did you know that Jupiter has 64 moons? Help steer the friends around them all.

DID YOU SPOT?

Europa the icy moon

Io the volcanic moon

Callisto the ancient moon

The Lord of the Rings

Spacecrafts can easily crash and burn in Saturn's rings.
Guide our friends safely through to the surface of Saturn.

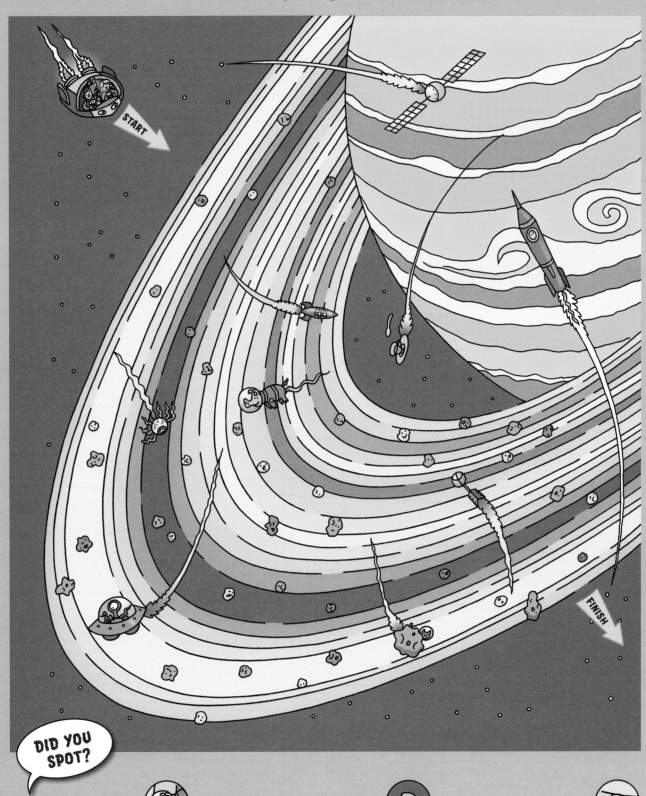

The space pig   The flying cup and saucer   The smiley meteorite

Stormy Sea

The shuttle switches to underwater mode on Neptune. Can you spot any star pieces?

The Uncanny Planet

Uranus is covered in mist and is not a very nice place.
The gang decides to hurry back to the shuttle.

DID YOU SPOT?

The ski goggles

The abandoned spaceship

The dark, cloaked figure

Play on Pluto

Our friends have arrived on Pluto, the number one sports venue in the galaxy, and two teams are about to play Spaceball! Help them get to their seats.

DID YOU SPOT?

The pair of green hover boots   The referee   A Venusian

Chapter 4

BEYOND THE MILKY WAY

Max, Millie, and Mojo are pleased to have found two star pieces in the Solar System. There are still three left to find, and the Universe is a big place!

Hyperspace

There is no time to lose, so the aliens decide to jump into hyperspace so they can travel at the speed of light! Help them navigate around the stars.

DID YOU SPOT?

A starship   A supersonic sheep   A Wrigglemonster

Milky Way

It takes a long time to get out of the Milky Way galaxy and into deep space.
Guide the spaceship through the spiral.

Traffic Jam

Oh no! There is a big traffic jam on the Andromeda Highway!
Guide the shuttle through all the other spaceships.

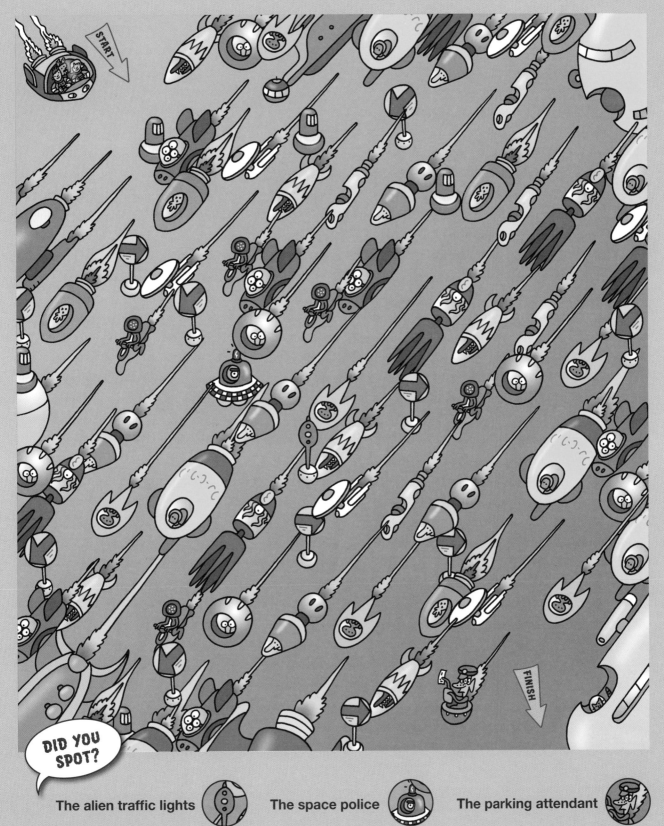

DID YOU SPOT?

The alien traffic lights   The space police   The parking attendant

Nebula

The friends decide to search a star nursery, where baby stars are born. To get there they have to go right into the middle of a nebula. Can you steer them in?

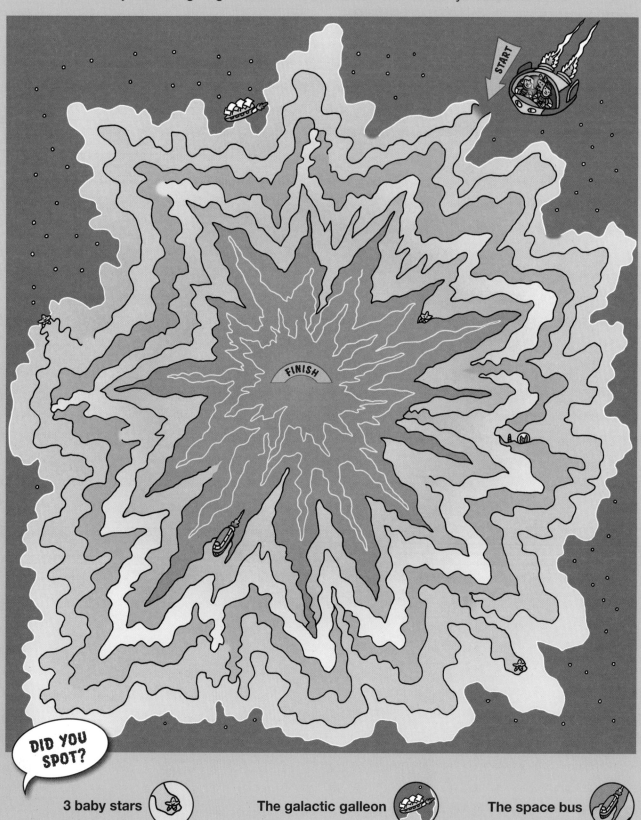

3 baby stars   The galactic galleon   The space bus

Star Nursery

This is one of the brightest places in the Universe, so put your starglasses on!

START

FINISH

DID YOU SPOT?

The teddy bear   A pair of lost starglasses   2 baby bottles

Alien Drive-In

Next stop, a drive-in space movie! The friends fly around the audience asking if anyone has news of the star pieces.

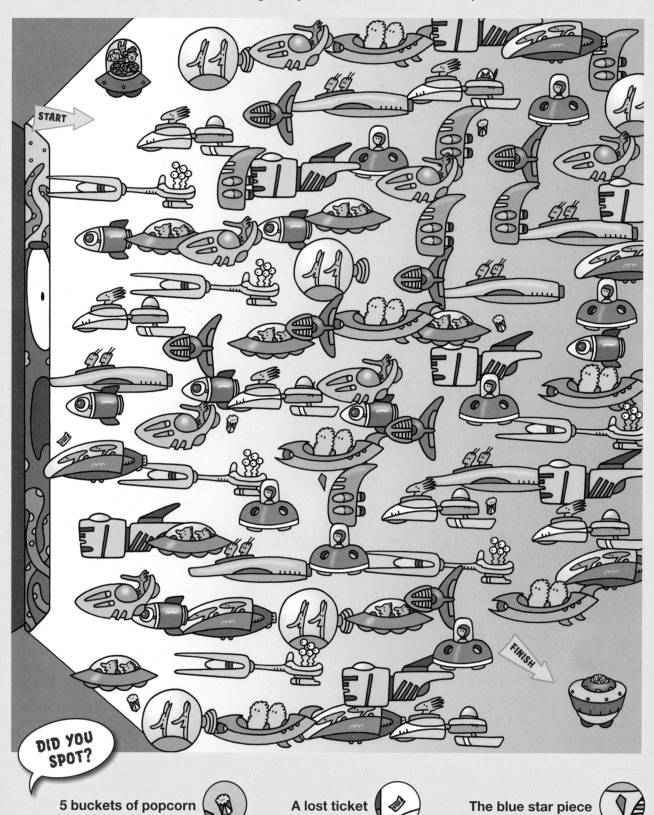

START

FINISH

DID YOU SPOT?

5 buckets of popcorn

A lost ticket

The blue star piece

Theme Park Thrills

An alien amusement park is very different from the ones back on Earth!
Help Max, Millie, and Mojo find a way through.

DID YOU SPOT?

The blue fish   The alien balloon   The pink cotton candy

Chapter 5

TIME IS RUNNING OUT!

The aliens can see that some stars are starting to fade. It's urgent that they collect all the star pieces! They have heard that the Zoid aliens from the planet Zosma are the ones who stole the star pieces, so they decide to go there to find them.

Inside the Cruiser

The aliens' little spaceship could not manage the huge journey to Zosma on its own, so they have hitched a lift on an intergalactic Space Cruiser! Max, Millie, and Mojo want to go up to the star deck.

DID YOU SPOT?

A Venusian   An arcade game   A purple alien

Giant Spaceport

The cruiser lands at a giant spaceport near Zosma.
Help the gang find their way back to their spaceship.

DID YOU SPOT?

The alien cat in a box   The alien with a purple belly   The human

Suspects' Planet

Our friends arrive at the planet Zosma but the Zoids fire so many missiles up at them that they can't land! Help them to dodge the missiles and get away.

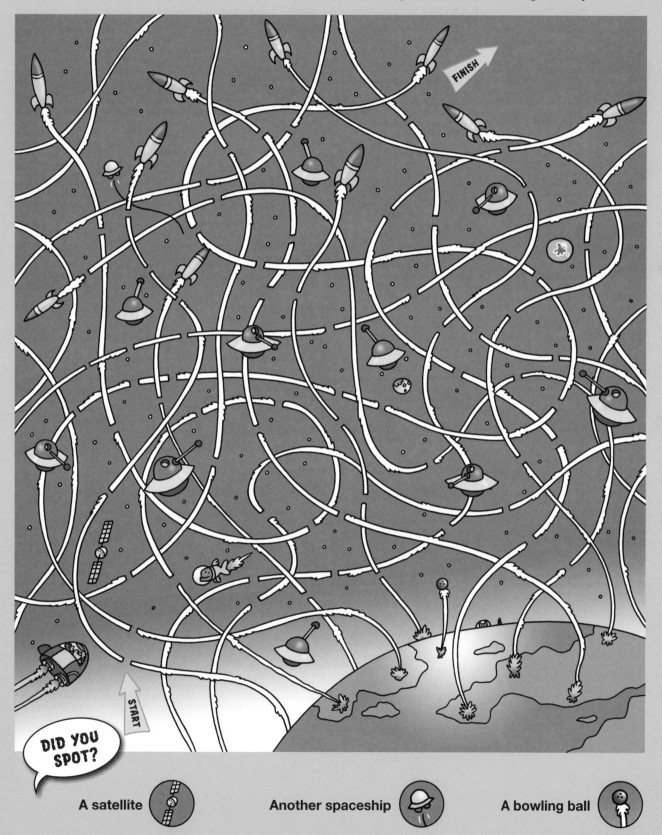

Spacewalk

The ship sustained some damage from the Zoid missiles. Help the gang spacewalk from the hatch to the broken bit to repair it.

Sudden Supernova!

A nearby star suddenly explodes, creating a supernova! Help our friends get away.

The space fire truck   The silly scientist   The frazzled fish

Supermassive Black Hole

The gang couldn't get away fast enough and are being sucked into a supermassive black hole! Help them avoid all the objects being sucked in with them.

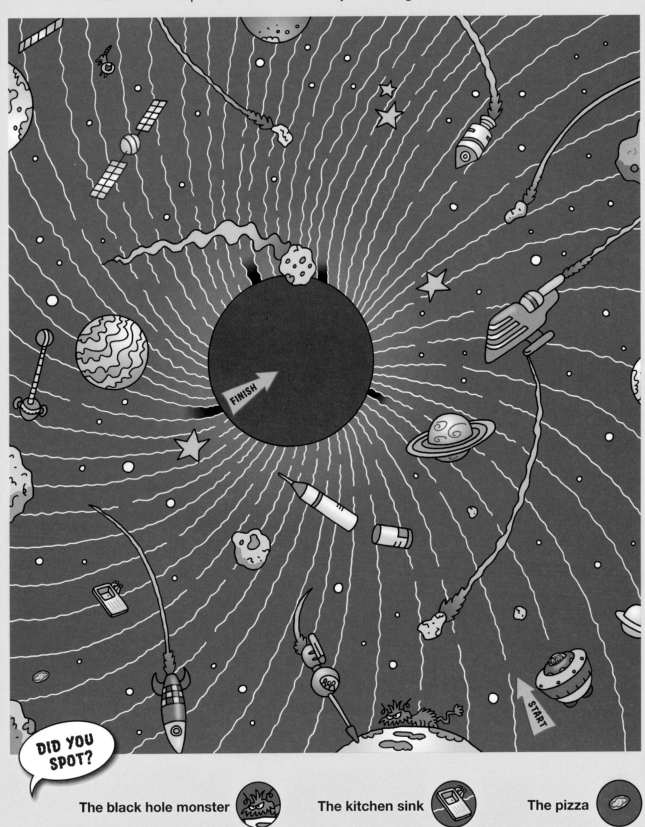

The black hole monster   The kitchen sink   The pizza

The Edge of the Universe

The black hole has spat our friends out at the very edge
of the Universe – an extremely strange place indeed!

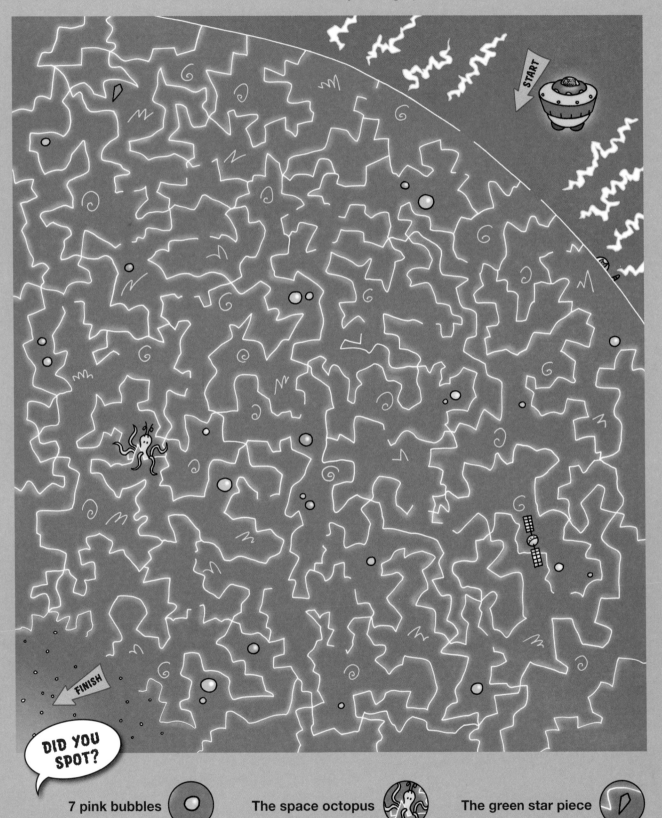

DID YOU SPOT?

7 pink bubbles   The space octopus   The green star piece

Chapter 6

HELP IS AT HAND

The aliens decide they need to go to the Capital of the Universe and ask the ruler, President Zendergast, to help them find the last star piece.

Wormhole

The fastest way to the Capital is through a wormhole, but watch out for space worms!

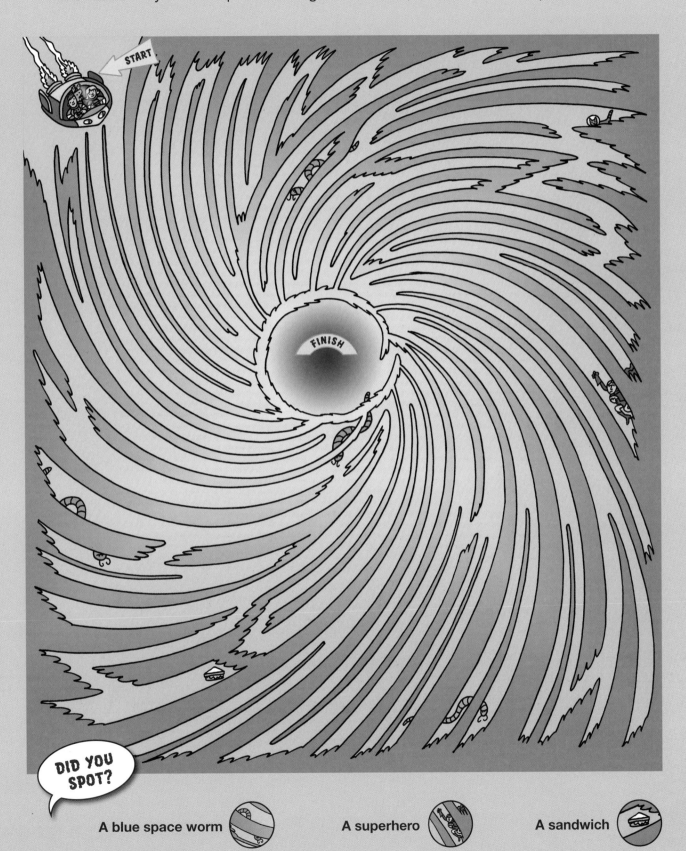

Which Way?

The inside of a wormhole can be a confusing place! Make sure our heroes go the right way.

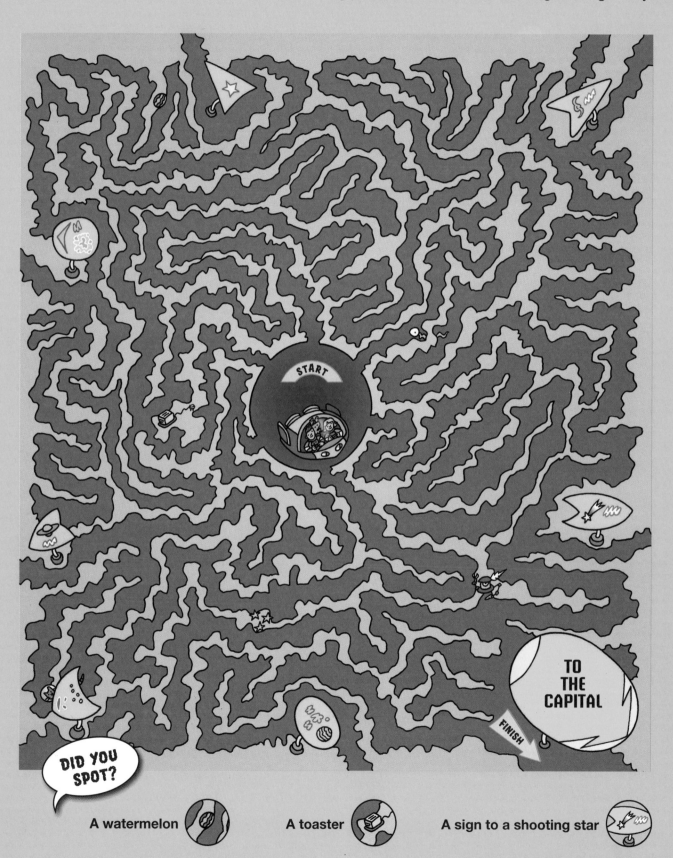

The Capital of the Universe

The friends have arrived at the Capital! But they need to pass through all the checkpoints before they are allowed to approach the planet.

DID YOU SPOT?

A galactic princess

A cone with a purple stripe

A flying saucer

On the Ground

Max, Millie, and Mojo would love to take in all the strange sights, but they must hurry along the space roads to see President Zendergast.

FINISH

START

DID YOU SPOT?

The space police

The green spaceship

The sign to the burger joint

Tall Tower

At last, the friends have made it to the tower where President Zendergast lives.
Find a way to the top.

Line Jump!

There are hundreds of people waiting to talk to the President so our friends have to dash around the barriers and jump the line before it's too late!

FINISH

START

DID YOU SPOT?

4 potato men

An alien in a baseball cap

The mutant banana

Jet Chase

Through the window of the President's tower, the gang spots a Zoid flying away with the final star piece! They put on jet packs to chase after him.

DID YOU SPOT?

3 beautiful butterflies

A bewildered bat

A broken biplane

Chapter 7
THIS MEANS WAR!

Max, Millie, and Mojo couldn't catch up with the crafty Zoid. But he's sent a message challenging our heroes to a battle for the final star piece. They need to find some friends to help them defeat the Zoids once and for all!

The Lazons

The Lazon aliens make the best laser guns in the Universe and have agreed to help fight the Zoids. Help guide Max, Millie, and Mojo safely through the laser beams.

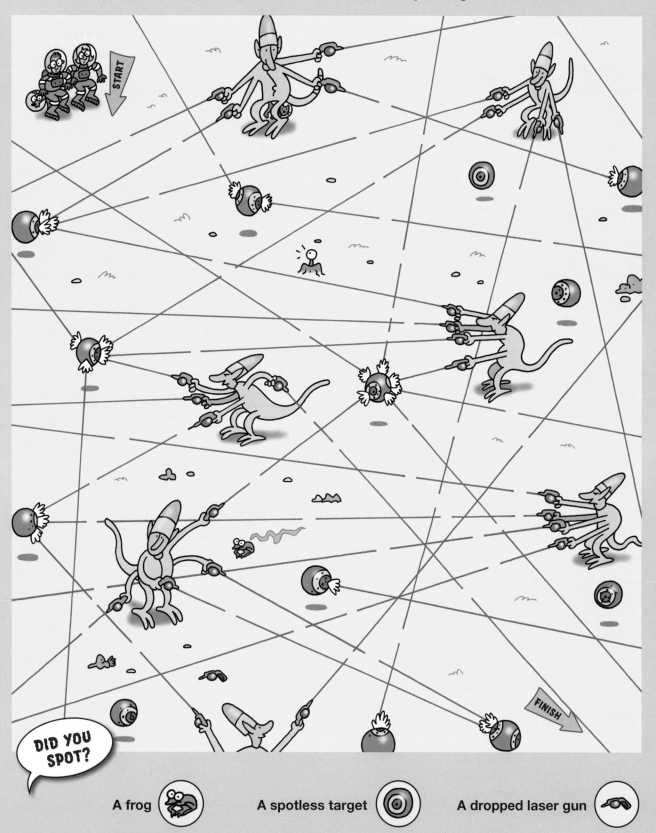

DID YOU SPOT?

A frog   A spotless target   A dropped laser gun

Intergalactic Travels

The gang needs to whizz around the galaxies to find more people to help them!

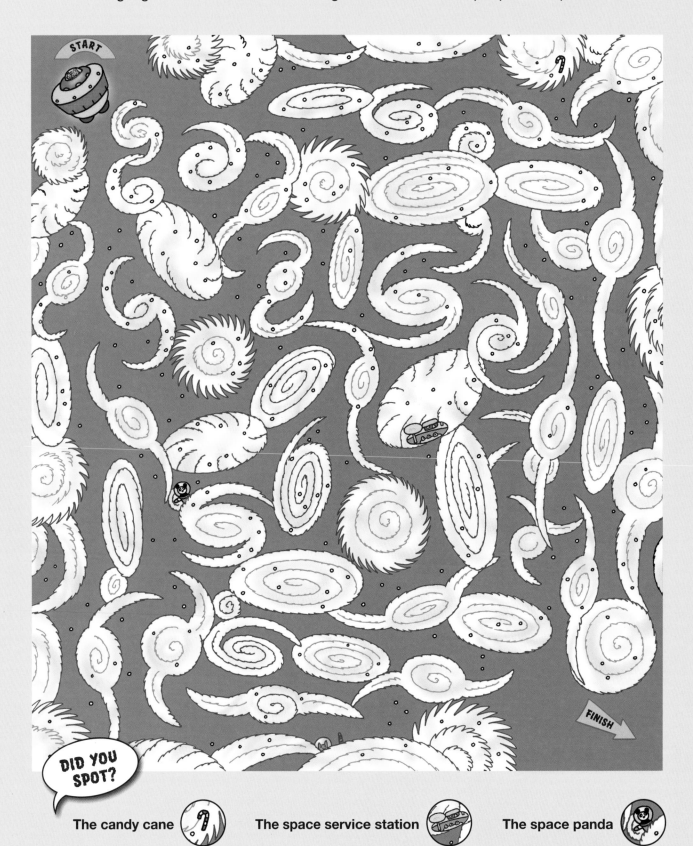

The candy cane   The space service station   The space panda

Frozen Planet

The gang arrives on a planet of ice and snow inhabited by the Wubbles.
Help them find a route to the Wubble mayor to ask for help.

DID YOU SPOT?

The Wubble fishing   **A white-bellied Wubble**   **The yeti footprint**

Star Surfers

Next, the gang tries to recruit the star surfers who hang out near the Orion Nebula.

DID YOU SPOT?

3 space jellyfish   The star helmet   The green surfboard

Squid Planet

The gang has a limited air supply, so they can't spend too much time underwater on Planet Squid. Help them find the leader quickly!

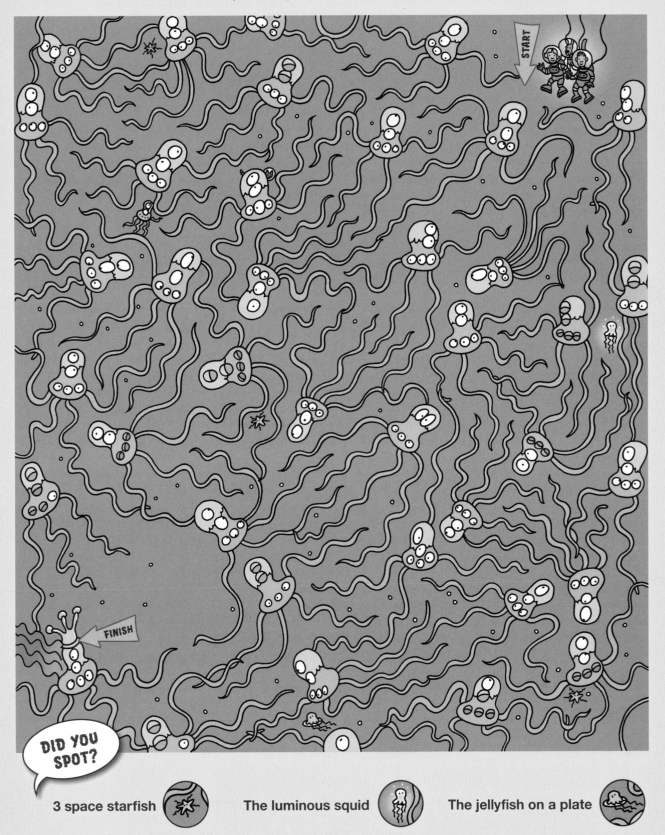

DID YOU SPOT?

3 space starfish   The luminous squid   The jellyfish on a plate

Crab Nebula

The clicky crabs of the Crab Nebula promise that they will help in the battle.

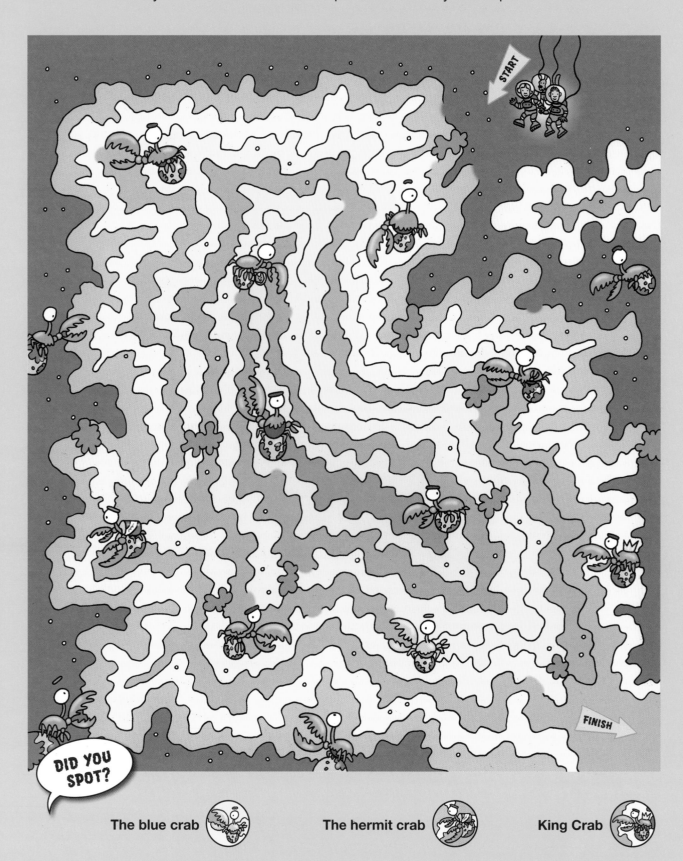

Neutron Star

Our friends need to get some ammunition for the battle. Help them collect one of the most explosive things in the Universe – the core of a neutron star.

DID YOU SPOT?

3 horseshoe magnets

A red rocket

A box of matches

Mojo the Mechanic

Mojo is the only one small enough to wriggle through the engine and put the neutron star piece in the firing tube.

DID YOU SPOT?

A tool box

3 bolts

Army Formation

When the gang arrives at the battle arena, everyone else is already there! Steer the shuttle to the front.

DID YOU SPOT?

Soldier Spider

Combat Duck

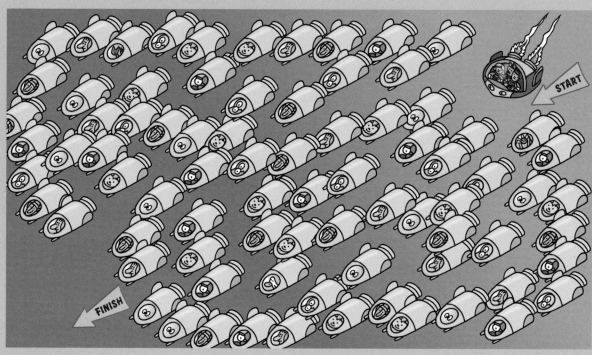

136

Star Quest

While everyone is distracted by the battle, Max, Millie, and Mojo
steer their shuttle to the Zoid's base to steal back the last star piece!

DID YOU SPOT?

An alien ejecting   A ball   The yellow star piece

Chapter 8

SAVING THE UNIVERSE

Hooray! Max, Millie, and Mojo have the final star piece. Now all they need to do is put the Mother Star back together.

Garbage Dump

Max, Millie, and Mojo are on their way back with the star piece to meet the aliens when they take a wrong turn and end up at an alien garbage dump!

DID YOU SPOT?

3 alien dump dwellers   The trash collector   A dumped diamond

Turn on the Lights

The gang needs to attach their star pieces and then light the flame at the core of the Mother Star. They've nearly done it!

DID YOU SPOT?

Space angler fish 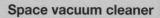 **Space vacuum cleaner**   **Space blimp**

Hungry Heroes

President Zendergast throws a banquet in honor of Max, Millie, and Mojo to say thank you for saving the Universe. And best of all, he gives Max and Millie a baby star each to take home!

DID YOU SPOT?

2 aliens with 5 eyes   Alien cakes   2 alien drinks

Galactic Gift

Max, Millie, and Mojo are taken to the best spaceship factory in the Universe, where they are given their very own spaceship!

DID YOU SPOT?

A ghost in the machine The factory boss 4 star-shaped screws

Journey Home

It is time for the trio to fly themselves home in their brand new spaceship. All their friends come out to say goodbye.

DID YOU SPOT?

The alien in a balloon   A baseball cap   A Wubble head balloon

Blue Planet

The friends need to make sure they land in the right place – Earth is a big planet!
Guide them to their destination.

144

Big Cat Jump

Ted, the ginger cat has decided to parachute home. Help him land safely.

Dizzy Mojo

Mojo feels very dizzy after all that space travel! Help him navigate his way out of the spaceship.

145

Home Sweet Home

The friends are very glad to be back on Earth, but they need to collect their tent before they can go home.

Shooting Stars

It's time for the baby stars to go to their new home in the sky above Max, Millie, and Mojo's house. One has already made it, but can you help the other one through the fireworks?

DID YOU SPOT?

A star nurse

A rainbow firework

A wise old owl

TIME
TRAVEL
MAZES

CONTENTS

Chapter 1
A Magic Machine

Keep looking out for Ted, the ginger cat. He's hitched a ride and will pop up in every maze!

Back home on Earth, Max, Millie, and Mojo are visiting a museum. Mojo wants to see the dinosaur bones first! But little do they know that their fun day will soon turn into an amazing adventure through time!

Museum Muddle

Today

Guide the gang through the giant dinosaur fossils. Max would love to see a real dinosaur.
You never know, his wish just might come true!

DID YOU SPOT?

The tiny mouse　　**2 spiders**　　**2 sets of false teeth**

Medieval Madness!

They'll have to be careful making their way through this collection of scary medieval exhibits. It's full of sharp swords, axes, and daggers.

DID YOU SPOT?

3 dropped gauntlets

The horse anklet

2 jewel-encrusted swords

Travels Through Time

It's a room filled with amazing machines from the past. But what's that mysterious box in the next room? Help the gang find a path through to it.

DID YOU SPOT?

The dropped helmet   The alien   3 dropped coffee cups

153

The Time Machine

As they stand in front of the box, it suddenly opens to reveal something quite extraordinary – a real-life time machine! The gang can't wait to have a look.

Taking Control!

Max, Millie, and Mojo are sitting in the time machine, trying to figure out how to make it work. It's very complicated! Can you find the way through the controls to the "on" switch?

154

Time Tumble

Oh no! The time machine has taken off, and Max and Millie are now whizzing through time. But Mojo has been thrown clear of the craft. Help him get back to the others.

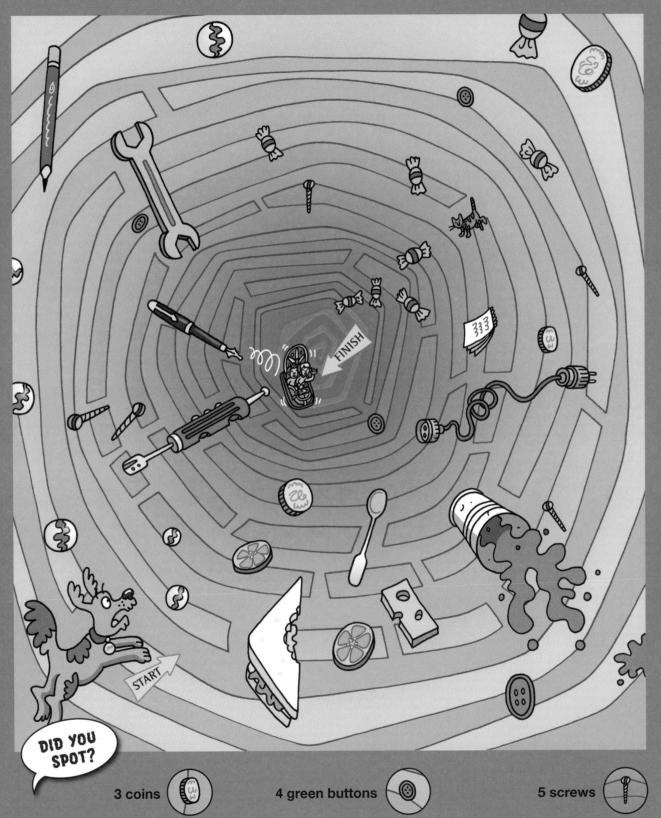

DID YOU SPOT?

3 coins   4 green buttons   5 screws

Crash Landing

What a strange place! The time machine has crash landed thousands of years in the future. It seems to be broken. What will they do? Perhaps there's someone in that big palace who can fix it.

DID YOU SPOT?

The hoverboard   2 flying cars   6 robots

Future Fix

The leader of the future city may look scary, but she's really very nice and is happy to help the gang. Guide them through the palace workshop to where the robots are fixing their craft.

The year 4500

DID YOU SPOT?

The dropped wrench   2 robot dogs   4 sonic screwdrivers

Chapter 2
Monster Mayhem

The time machine is working again, but the lever to take the gang back to the present is broken. That means they must either go into the future or into the past. They decide to head back to the past. Maybe they can find someone to fix the controls – and have a few adventures on the way!

Ferny Forest

Max and Millie set the controls for "long ago" and have landed in a hot, steamy forest. Where and when are they? Time to do some exploring. Help them through the ferns to the jungle clearing.

DID YOU SPOT?

The bird's nest   3 bumble bees   3 blue feathers

159

Dino Dodge

There are dinosaurs everywhere! Maybe they should visit another age where they're not so likely to end up as a dino's dinner. Help them tiptoe through the battling beasts.

160

Mud Bath

Max, Millie, and Mojo have fallen into this muddy swamp, but they can see the time machine on the other side! Time to swim for it.

70 million years ago

START

FINISH

DID YOU SPOT?

2 purple turtles   3 sleek snakes   3 dino footprints

Mammoths on the March

The time machine has whisked our friends further forward in time to the Ice Age.
Help them across the snow and through this huge herd of marching mammoths.

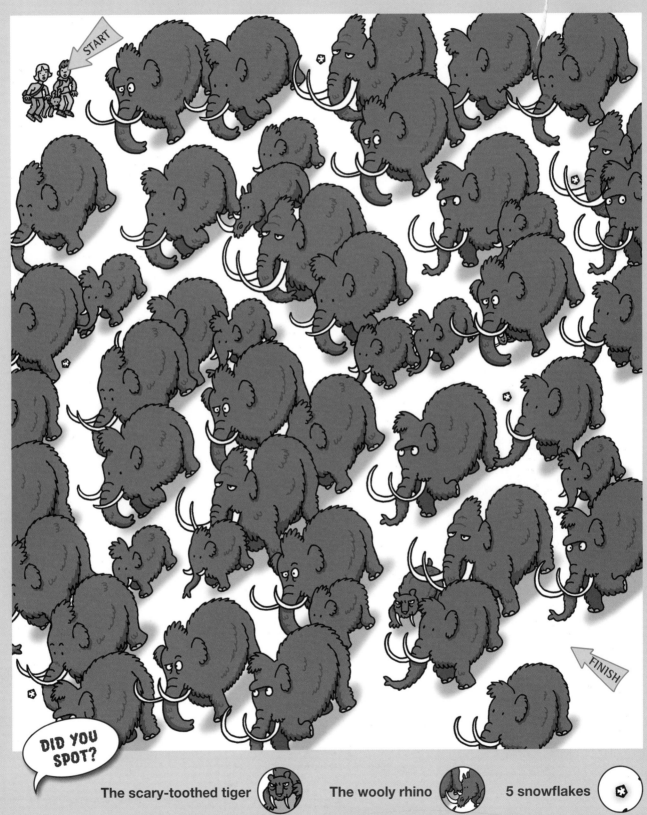

162

Painted Cave

Brrr, it's cold! The gang has climbed into a cave to get warm. Can you trace a path through the cave paintings to the entrance where the time machine is waiting?

20,000 years ago

DID YOU SPOT?

The strange statue

The paint pot

3 brushes

The year 2500 BCE

Standing Stones

This must be the Stone Age. And there are some Stone Age people! Perhaps one of them can help. Can you pick a path through the giant monuments?

DID YOU SPOT?

3 axes

4 arrowheads

4 rabbits

Contour Challenge

Mojo has run off and now he's stuck on the top of this burial mound.
Help him rejoin the gang at the bottom.

DID YOU SPOT?

2 skulls

3 weasels

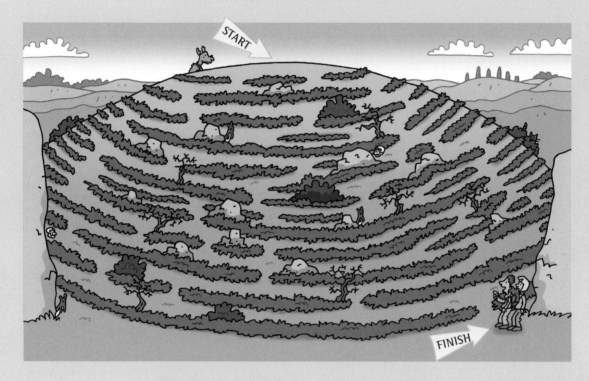

On the Farm

Max, Millie, and Mojo have arrived at a farm. The farmers think the village chief across
the river might be able to help. Guide the gang through the field to the boat.

DID YOU SPOT?

3 crows

3 baskets

165

Down the River

The year 2500 BCE

Down the River

Help the gang paddle their canoe across the busy, fast-flowing river to the village.
Watch out for the jumping fish!

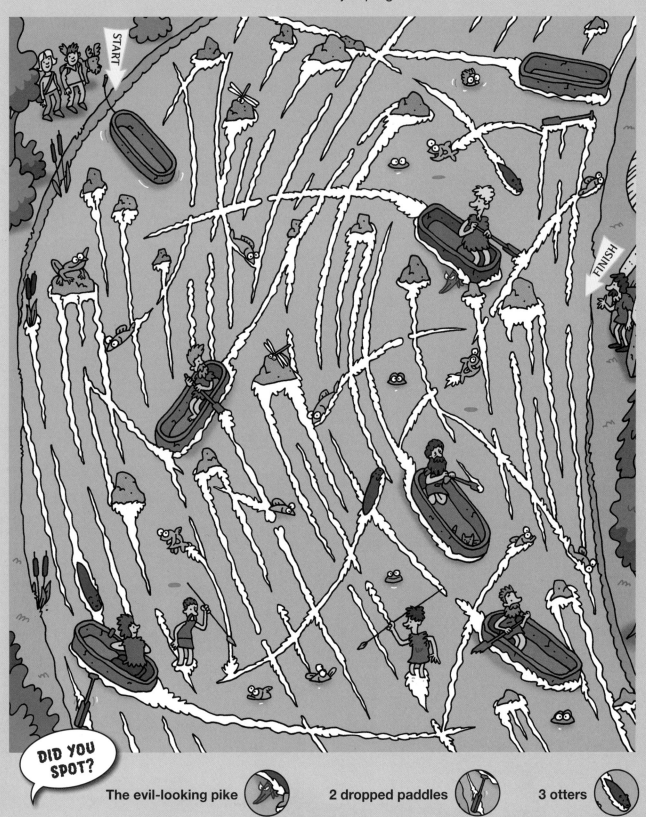

DID YOU SPOT?

The evil-looking pike   2 dropped paddles   3 otters

166

Village Life

Max, Millie, and Mojo need to find their way through the Stone Age huts to where the village chief is waiting for them.

START

FINISH

DID YOU SPOT?

The cooking pot   The pig   3 stone axes

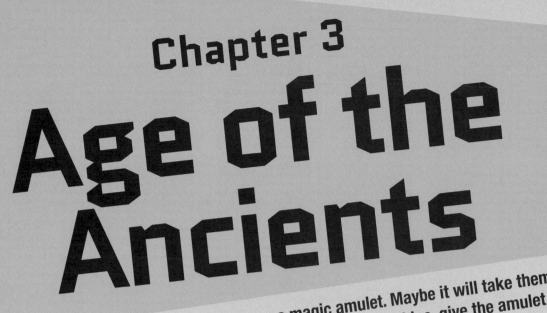

Chapter 3
Age of the Ancients

The village chief has given the gang a magic amulet. Maybe it will take them back to the present. They climb back into the time machine, give the amulet a rub, and adjust the controls. Where will they end up?

Land of the Pharaohs

This isn't the present! The gang has been whisked into the future, but only to the time of ancient Egypt. Help them climb the pyramid to see the pharaoh. Maybe he'll know what to do.

DID YOU SPOT?

The sphinx

3 sinister birds

3 obelisks

169

The Future is Written

The pharaoh has told them to go inside the pyramid and look at these hieroglyphics. Wow!
The story seems to be about the gang. Can you get to the end and find out what's going to happen?

DID YOU SPOT?

The snake symbol   4 lion symbols   5 hand symbols

170

Going for Gold

The gang has jumped forward in time to ancient Greece, but the time machine has gone missing! Help them run through these competitors at the Olympic Games so they can look for it.

START

FINISH

DID YOU SPOT?

The trumpet

The Olympic flame

4 discs

171

The Temple of Zeus

It's a giant temple filled with statues. Our friends want to find their way to the mysterious door by the statue of Zeus, the leader of the Greek gods.

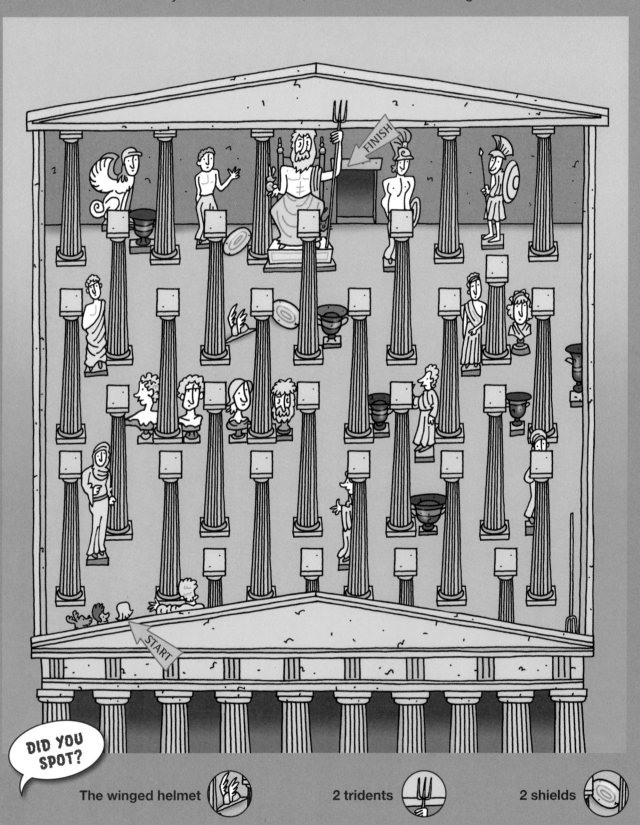

DID YOU SPOT?

The winged helmet   2 tridents   2 shields

172

Into the Labyrinth

The year 400 BCE

The time machine was stolen by the minotaur, a scary monster that's half bull, half human. The gang will have to be careful finding their way through the labyrinth to get it back.

FINISH

START

DID YOU SPOT?

The ball of string   2 swords   3 burning torches

173

On the March!

The gang has now landed in ancient Rome. They've decided to find the emperor to ask his advice. But first they need to weave their way through all these marching soldiers.

START

FINISH

DID YOU SPOT?

The eagle standard   The catapult   3 plumed helmets

174

Roman Run

There's the emperor! But to reach him, the gang is going to have to tiptoe through all these fierce gladiators and animals fighting in the Colosseum.

The year 100

DID YOU SPOT?

The lute

The bag of coins

8 dropped shields

The Silk Road

The Roman emperor can't help them. He's told them to head down a long and winding path known as the Silk Road to China to find the emperor there.

DID YOU SPOT?

The elephant   4 camels   5 silk moths

176

Boom!

The Chinese emperor has welcomed the gang with a party and lots of fireworks. They've been fired up into the sky on a rocket. Guide them down to the time machine. Careful now!

The year 800

The pink and yellow rocket　　**The panda**　　**3 bats**

Chapter 4
Around the Castles

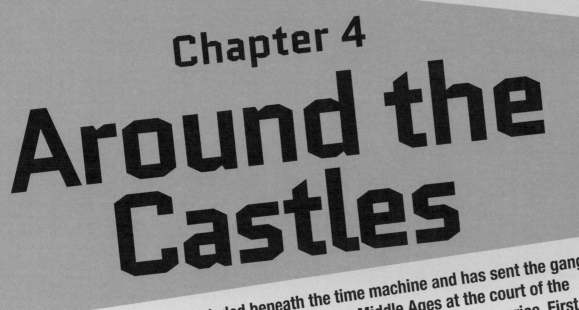

One of the fireworks exploded beneath the time machine and has sent the gang flying into the future. They've landed in the Middle Ages at the court of the English king, Henry VIII. He's promised to help the gang – but at a price. First, they'll have to travel around the medieval world, collecting as much treasure as they can for the greedy king.

Viking Raid

The first stop is back to the age of the Vikings. These fearsome warriors from Scandinavia have left some treasure behind for our friends. Help them find it.

The year 1000

DID YOU SPOT?

The trumpet   The helmet with the upside down horn   4 seals

Charge!

Our friends have gone looking for jewels in Central Asia, and now they need to get back to their time machine. But first they must cross the fierce, charging horsemen of Genghis Khan.

DID YOU SPOT?

The helmet with two points   3 eagles   The blue flag

180

Fortress City

Our friends are at the crossroads of Europe and Asia in Constantinople, one of the most heavily defended cities in the world. A reward awaits them in the middle, if they can dodge the guards.

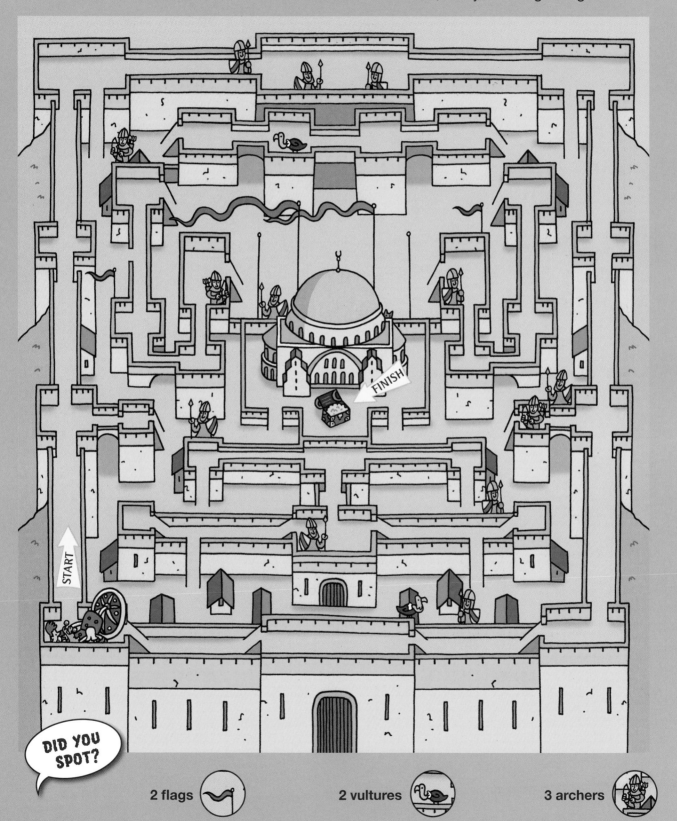

DID YOU SPOT?

2 flags   2 vultures   3 archers

Art Attack

On their way back to England, the gang has decided to stop off in Italy during the Renaissance.
They're going to get the famous artist Michelangelo to paint them a picture.

DID YOU SPOT?

The pot of paint   2 dropped chisels   3 dropped paintbrushes

Sent to the Tower

The final stop on the gang's Medieval World tour is the Tower of London.
Help them climb its walls to collect the treasure on the roof.

FINISH

START

DID YOU
SPOT?

2 polar bears   3 scary knights   5 ravens

Lance-A-Lot

Max, Millie, and Mojo are finally back at the court of Henry VIII where an exciting jousting tournament is taking place. The king should be delighted with all that treasure.

START

FINISH

DID YOU SPOT?

The dropped gauntlet

2 pet falcons

2 swords on the ground

Hampton Court Maze

What's this? Henry has hidden the time machine in the middle of his own maze.
Mojo has found it. Can Max and Millie get there too?

Chapter 5
The New World

To get to the present, the king thinks the gang should first head back into the past to find the most famous explorer of all time – Christopher Columbus. He was the first European to set eyes on the Americas – so if anyone will know how to get somewhere, it's surely him. But they'll have to find him first, and that means heading west to the New World.

Big Heads

The gang has arrived in what is now Mexico. These giant heads were carved thousands of years ago by the Olmecs, one of the first great civilizations of the Americas.

The year 1492

START

FINISH

DID YOU SPOT?

The jaguar   2 jade masks   4 monkeys

187

City of the Aztecs

The gang has made its way to Tenochtitlan, the capital city of the Aztecs. Guide them through the streets to the emperor. Maybe he'll know where Columbus is.

DID YOU SPOT?

The calendar stone   2 eagles   3 snakes

The Ball Game

The emperor has challenged the gang to a friendly ball game. Our friends need to slam dunk a rubber ball into the stone ring before they can head on their way.

189

The Great Plains

Mojo's jumping skills helped them win the game, and now the gang is exploring North America. Maybe this Cheyenne chieftain will know where to find Columbus.

DID YOU SPOT?

5 baby bison

2 coyotes

3 cacti

Totem Poles

The year 1492

In the far northwest of America, our friends have come across a thick forest filled with towering totem poles carved by Native Americans. But still no sign of Columbus.

DID YOU SPOT?

2 canoes

3 beavers

The puma

Inca Fortress

The gang has headed to South America to the Inca fortress of Machu Picchu. The emperor has told our friends where to find Columbus – he's in the Caribbean. Now they must race back to the time machine.

START

FINISH

DID YOU SPOT?

The panpipe player   2 llamas   2 condors

192

All Aboard!

At last, the gang has found Columbus. Help them find their sea legs as they wriggle through the crew to the front of the boat.

The year 1492

DID YOU SPOT?

The map

3 seagulls

Lost at Sea

Oh dear. It seems that Columbus isn't such a great explorer after all. He's actually lost. Help him weave his way through the islands to the open sea.

The year 1492

DID YOU SPOT?

2 messages in bottles

4 flying fish

Chapter 6
Great Minds

Columbus couldn't help the gang get back to the present. So they're going to visit some of the greatest thinkers of the age to see if they know what to do. The first stop is Renaissance Italy, where they're hoping to meet the painter, inventor, scientist, and all-around clever cat, Leonardo da Vinci.

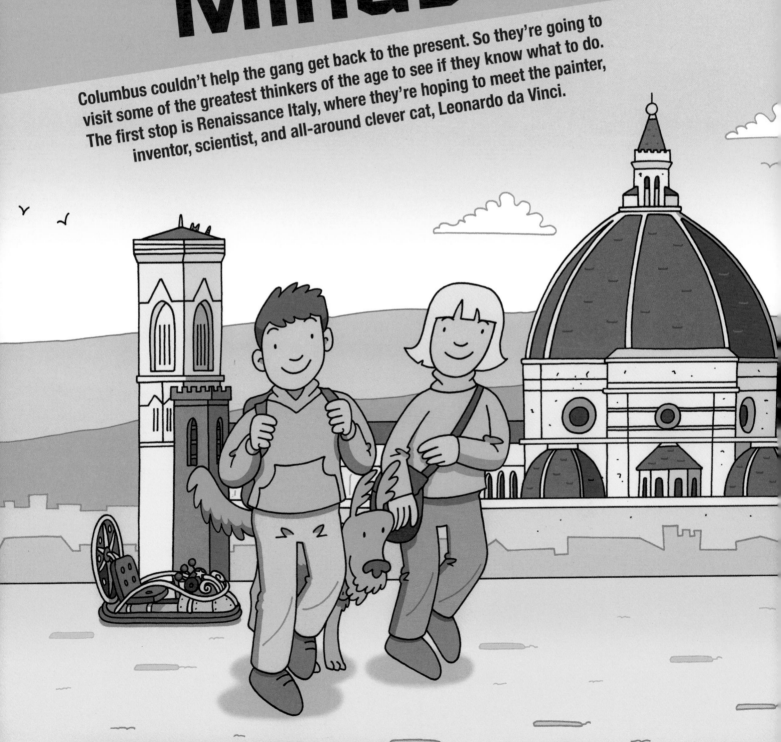

Ahead of his Time

Leonardo has invented many wonderful contraptions, including a tank, a helicopter, and a flying machine. Maybe he understands time machines too.

The year 1500

DID YOU SPOT?

The globe   The notebook   3 potion bottles

Take a Bow

They've drawn a blank in Italy, so it's time to tap some of England's great minds. Maybe William Shakespeare, the world famous playwright, can find the words to fix the time machine.

DID YOU SPOT?

The picture of Queen Elizabeth I   3 quill pens   3 candles

Falling Down

Now they need to dodge the falling apples to find Sir Isaac Newton, one of the greatest scientists of all time. He discovered the laws of gravity – perhaps he knows the laws of time too.

DID YOU SPOT?

The badger   2 owls   3 field mice

197

The Shocking Truth

The gang is back in the Americas. Help them through the lightning bolts to where the famous inventor, scientist, and politician Benjamin Franklin is conducting an electrical experiment.

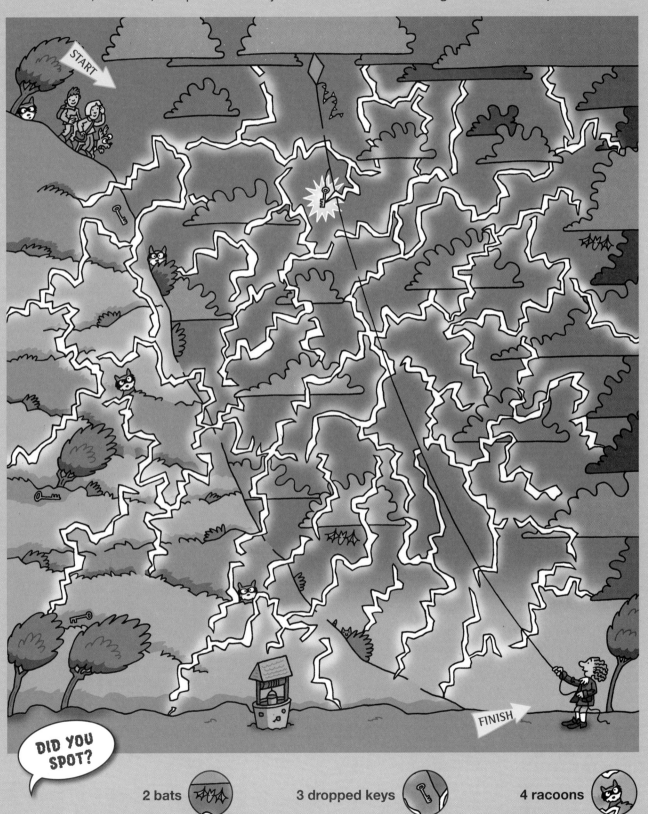

DID YOU SPOT?

2 bats   3 dropped keys   4 racoons

A Presidential Welcome

The year 1789

Franklin has sent them to find his friend, George Washington, the first President of the United States of America. Row them across the frozen river to where the president is waiting.

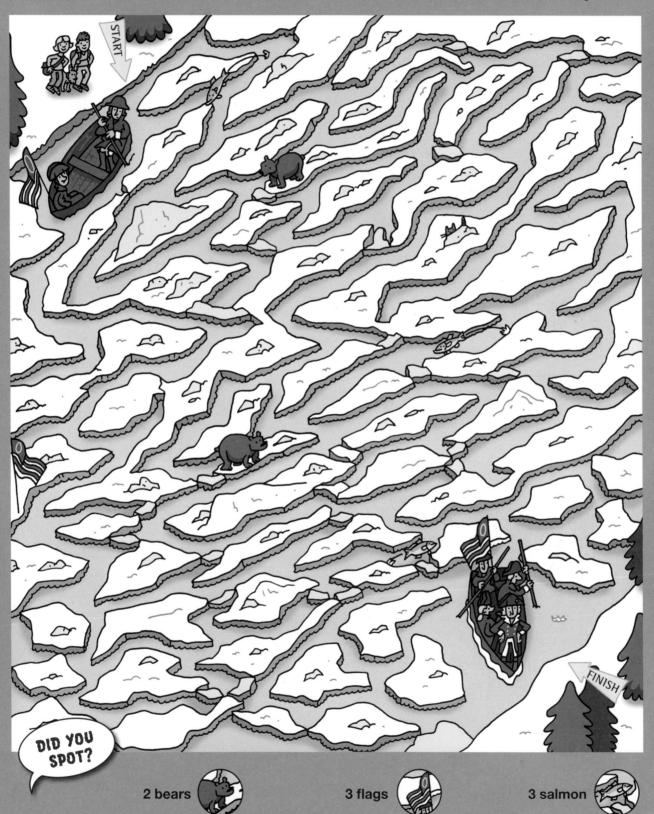

DID YOU SPOT?

2 bears   3 flags   3 salmon

A Trip to the Palace

Washington has sent them to France to see the wealthy king and queen, Louis XVI and Marie Antoinette. Maybe the royals can pay for the gang to get back to the present.

DID YOU SPOT?

2 spiders

3 crowns

Revolution!

Oops! Looks like the royals will have to run for it. The poor people of France have started a revolution to overthrow the monarchy. Help the gang escape back to the time machine.

DID YOU SPOT?

The plate of cakes

3 pigeons

200

Don't Get Blown Apart!

The gang is looking for Napoleon Bonaparte, the man who became the leader of France after the Revolution. One of the greatest generals in history, he might have a strategy for getting home.

DID YOU SPOT?

The eagle standard 2 white horses 3 drums

Chapter 7
The Age of Machines

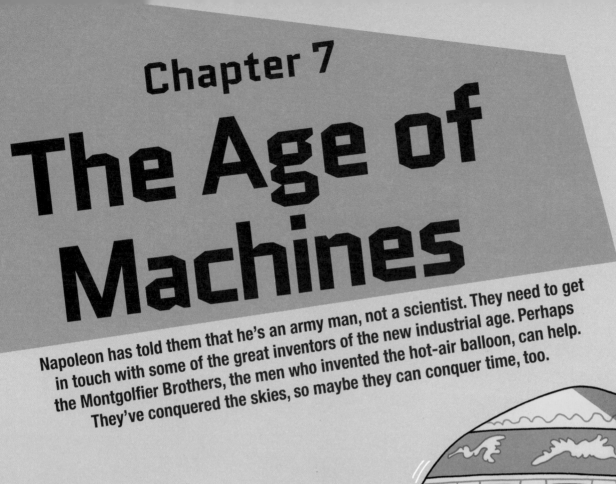

Napoleon has told them that he's an army man, not a scientist. They need to get in touch with some of the great inventors of the new industrial age. Perhaps the Montgolfier Brothers, the men who invented the hot-air balloon, can help. They've conquered the skies, so maybe they can conquer time, too.

Up in the Air

Help the Montgolfier brothers, Joseph and Jacques, carefully deliver Max, Millie, and Mojo back down to the time machine.

The year 1799

DID YOU SPOT?

The cow   2 rabbits   6 pigeons

Industrial Revolution

The brothers couldn't help, so the gang has traveled to Britain to find James Watt, the master of the new-fangled steam engine. Guide them through the smoking factory chimneys to his workshop.

DID YOU SPOT?

3 wheelbarrows   3 buckets   4 rats

Scaling the Steam Engine

The year 1800

There he is! Help our friends clamber up the enormous, whirring steam engine to where the great inventor is waiting. He tells them that they need to find an expert on vehicles.

DID YOU SPOT?

2 pairs of pliers

2 hammers

4 wrenches

Ship Shape

And there's one of the world's leading experts on vehicles, Isambard Kingdom Brunel, the designer of the "SS Great Eastern," the biggest ship in the world. What will he say?

Start Your Engines

Brunel has told them to find someone who knows about cars, not boats. So they're now in Germany to track down the pioneers of the motor car, Karl and Bertha Benz. There they are!

DID YOU SPOT?

The bicycle   2 spare tires   3 dropped cranks

Let There be Light

Still looking for an answer, the gang has crossed the Atlantic Ocean to meet Thomas Edison, the inventor of the light bulb. Maybe he'll have a bright idea!

DID YOU SPOT?

2 mice   3 moths   4 spiders

The Lightning Master

The year 1905

Edison has shown them where to find an even more talented scientist, a man who can actually control electricity, Nikola Tesla. Guide the gang to him through the giant sparks.

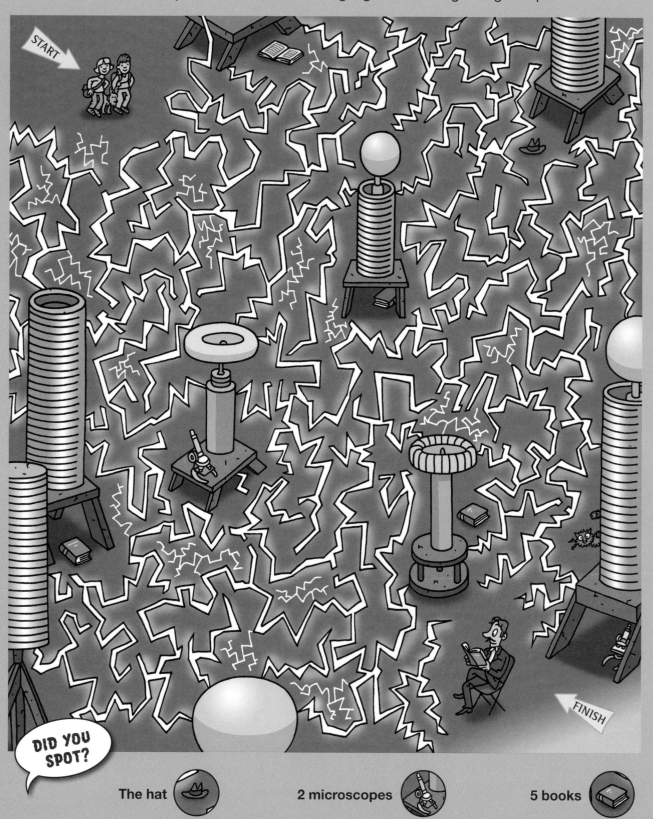

DID YOU SPOT?

The hat   2 microscopes   5 books

Chapter 8
Back to the Present

Even Nicola Tesla, the master of lightning, wasn't able to help them. But he's told them about a scientist who definitely can, the most famous scientist of all time — Albert Einstein. And Tesla has one more trick up his sleeve. He sends a powerful bolt of electricity toward the Time Machine. It buzzes and suddenly begins to hover — now the gang can fly!

Airship Odyssey

Max, Millie, and Mojo have taken to the skies on the search for Einstein. Help them weave and twist through these Zeppelins.

The year 1910

FINISH

START

DID YOU SPOT?

The green airship   2 spiders   3 parachutists

211

Plane Crazy

There's more air traffic for the gang to find a way through. Now the sky is filled with bi-planes. Guide them down to Wilbur and Orville Wright, the inventors of the plane.

START

FINISH

DID YOU SPOT?

The monkey co-pilot   The orange tail   4 wing walkers

212

Early Whirly Birds

Looks like the Wright brothers have put the gang on the right path. Steer them up through these early helicopters to the great astronomer, Edwin Hubble. He'll know where Einstein is.

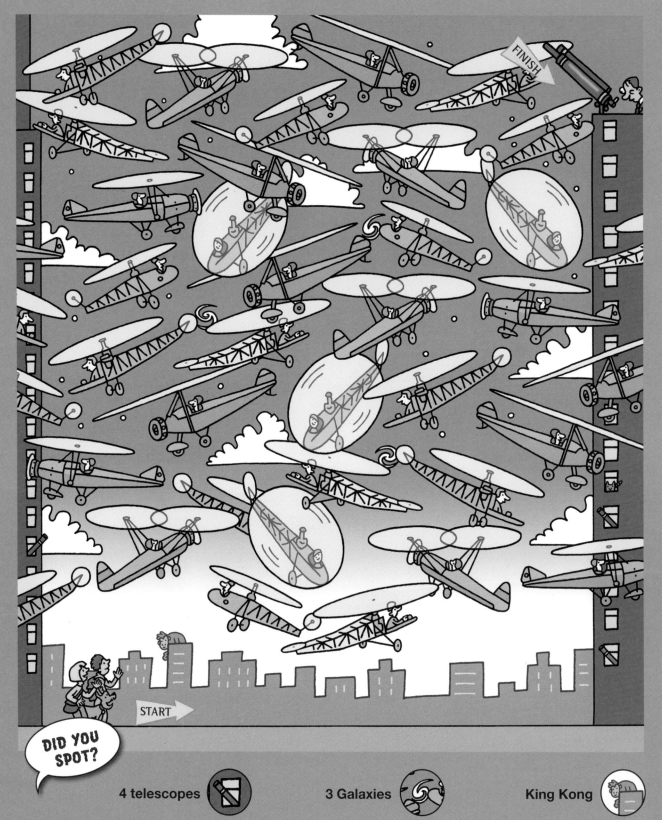

DID YOU SPOT?

4 telescopes

3 Galaxies

King Kong

I See (Through) You

Einstein is in the building, but first they need to pass through this science laboratory where Marie Curie is experimenting with radioactivity. Watch out for the X-Rays.

DID YOU SPOT?

2 petri dishes   3 dropped test tubes   3 pens

Easy Einstein

Professor Einstein has just finished giving a lecture. Help the gang through the audience to meet him.

Showing the Way

Einstein knows what to do! The gang must head to the Moon, where there's a time portal that will take them back to the present. Help them plan their route.

215

Race to the Moon

With their space helmets on, the gang is on their way to the Moon. But they must dodge all the super-speedy US and Soviet rockets that are trying to get there first.

The Way Home

They've made it to the portal! Now they must be sure to pick the right path back to the museum. Choose carefully now!

The year 1965

DID YOU SPOT?

The dropped helmet   2 meteorites   2 Moon spiders

217

Back with a Bump

At last! It's good to be back. Now they need to get the time machine back in its box. Help them push it through some rather familiar looking exhibits.

DID YOU SPOT?

A dinosaur tooth   2 quill pens   3 apples

Celebration Time!

Time to go home. Max, Millie, and Mojo are going to put the time machine in a storeroom and out of harm's way. Guide them to the exit where they can enjoy a well-earned ice cream!

DID YOU SPOT?

The fire extinguisher   2 security guards   3 dropped ice cream cones

Answers

Mazes Around the World

Northern ▶
Lights
page 7

◀Iceberg!
page 9

Going on a ▶
Bear Hunt!
page 8

◀Husky
Chase
page 10

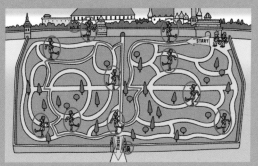

◀Moscow
March
page 11

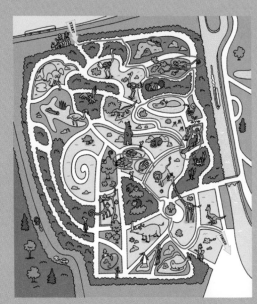

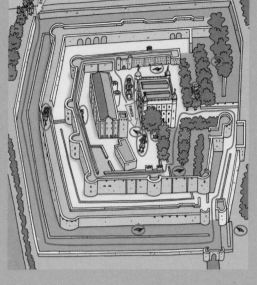

Acropolis ▶
page 21

◀ Sargasso
Sea
page 24

◀ The Devil's
Triangle
page 25

Leaving ▶
the Docks
page 23

◀ Cabin Fever
page 28

Shipping ▶
Lanes
page 24

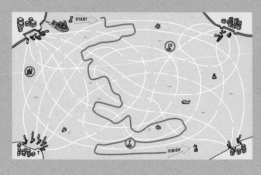

Battle the ▶
High Seas
page 27

◀Kidnapped
page 29

Shipwrecked▶
page 28

◀Niagara
page 31

◀Dinosaur
Dig
page 32

Cherokee ▶
Trail
page 33

◀ Cattle
Drive
page 36

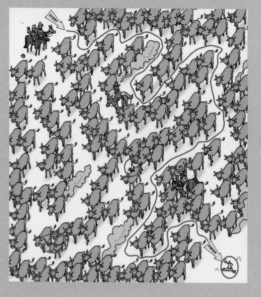

Swamped! ▶
page 34

◀ Medicine
Wheel
page 37

Tornado! ▶
page 35

◀ Mount
Rushmore
page 38

Yellowstone ▶
Park
page 38

◀ Carnival!
page 42

Rocky ▶
Road
page 39

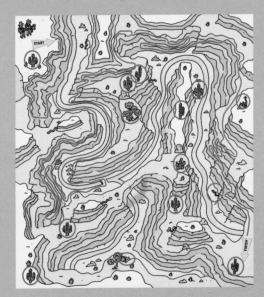

◀ Rainforest
Ramble
page 43

Mexican ▶
Temple
page 41

◀ Sink Hole
City
page 44

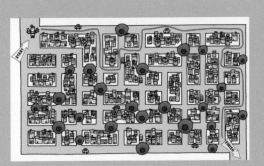

On Safari ▶
page 51

◀ Gorilla
Mountain
page 53

Watering ▶
Hole
page 52

◀ Riding the
Dunes
page 54

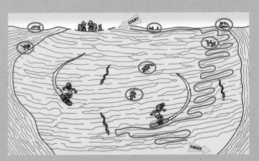
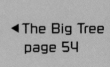

◀ The Big Tree
page 54

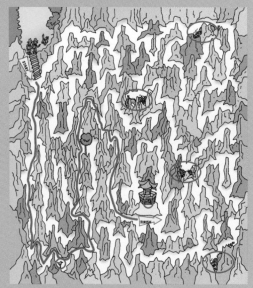

Hopalong! ▶
page 61

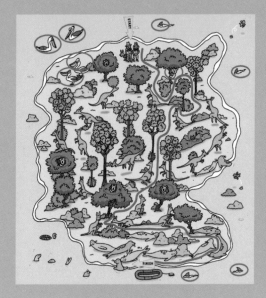

◀ Walkabout
page 63

Catch the ▶
Wave
page 62

◀ A Fishy
Puzzle
page 64

◀ Umbrella
Beach
page 64

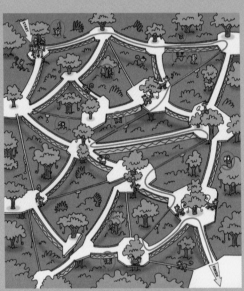
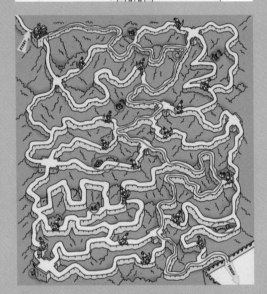

Mazes Across the Universe

Follow That ▶
Star
page 79

◀ Come and
Join Us
page 81

Mystery ▶
Craft
page 80

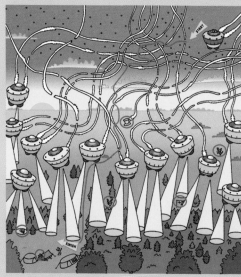

◀ Mojo's
Dash
page 82

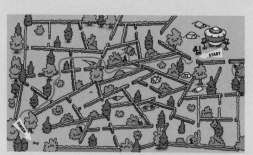

◀ Ginger Cat
Stowaway
page 82

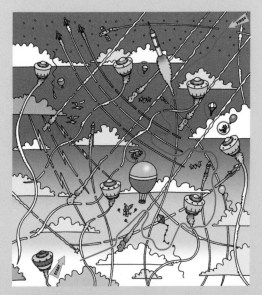

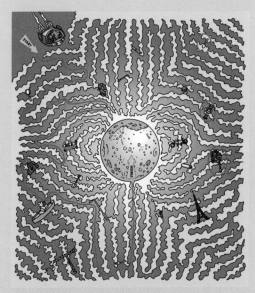

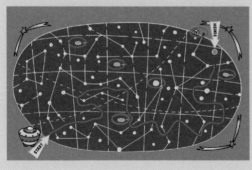

Alien ▶
Schooltime
page 95

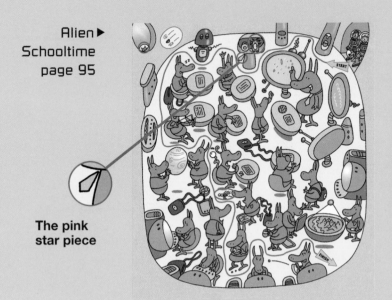

The pink
star piece

◀ Many Moons
page 99

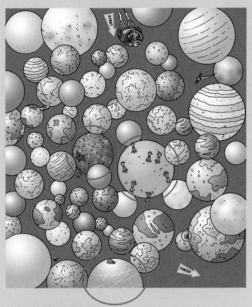

Asteroid ▶
Belt
page 97

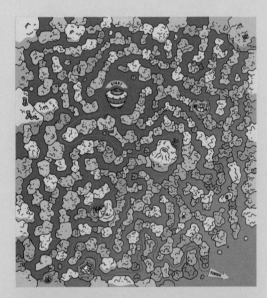

◀ The Lord of
the Rings
page 100

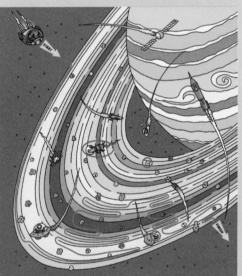

The Eye of ▶
Jupiter
page 98

Traffic ▶
Jam
page 107

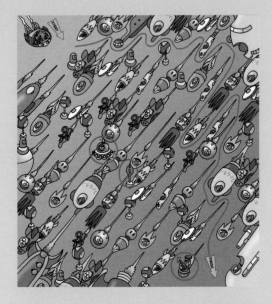

◀ Star Nursery
page 109

Nebula ▶
page 108

◀ Alien
Drive-In
page 110

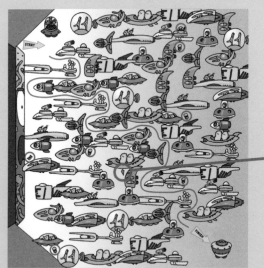

**The blue
star piece**

◀ Theme Park
Thrills
page 111

238

Inside the ▶
Cruiser
page 113

◀ Spacewalk
page 116

Giant ▶
Spaceport
page 114

◀ Sudden
Supernova
page 117

Suspects' ▶
Planet
page 115

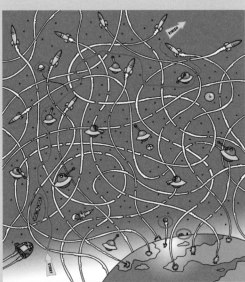

**Supermassive ▶
Black Hole
page 118**

◀Which
Way?
page 122

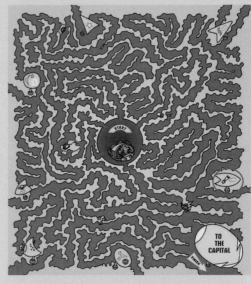

**The Edge of ▶
the Universe
page 119**

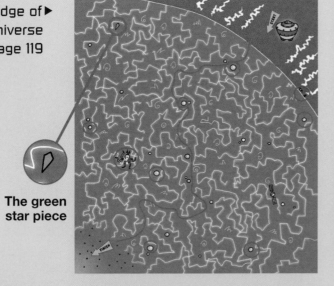

**The green
star piece**

◀The Capital of
the Universe
page 123

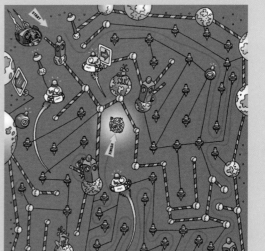

**Wormhole ▶
page 121**

240

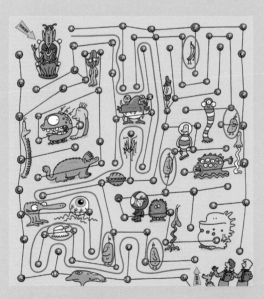

Intergalactic ▶
Travels
page 130

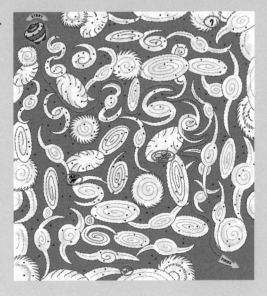

◀Squid Planet
page 133

Frozen▶
Planet
page 131

◀Crab Nebula
page 134

Star Surfers▶
page 132

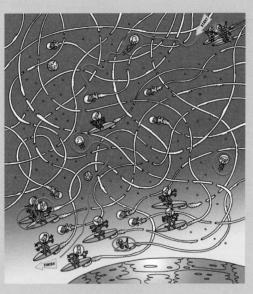

◀Neutron Star
page 135

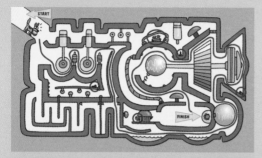

Mojo the ▶
Mechanic
page 136

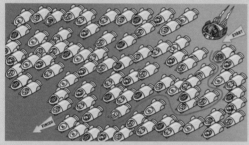

Army ▶
Formation
page 136

◀ Turn on the
Lights
page 140

Star ▶
Quest
page 137

he yellow
tar piece

◀ Hungry
Heroes
page 141

Garbage ▶
Dump
page 139

◀ Galactic
Gift
page 142

Time Travel Mazes

Museum ▶
Muddle
page 151

◀ Travels
Through Time
page 153

Medieval ▶
Madness
page 152

◀ The Time
Machine
page 154

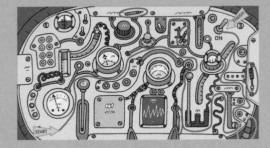
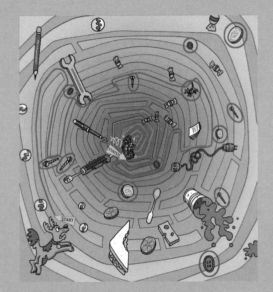

Dino Dodge ▶
page 160

◀ Painted
Cave
page 163

Mud Bath ▶
page 161

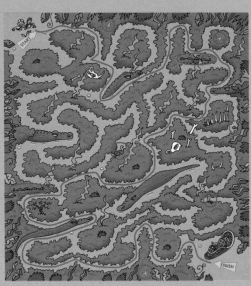

◀ Standing
Stones
page 164

◀Mammoths on ▶
the March
page 162

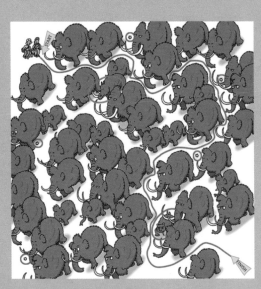

◀ Contour
Challenge
page 165

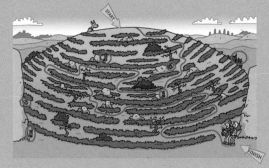

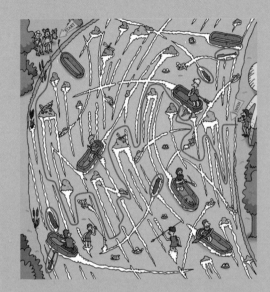

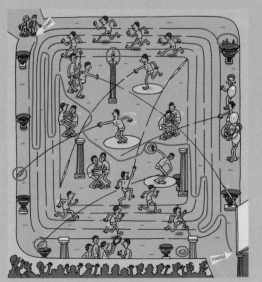

The Temple ▶
of Zeus
page 172

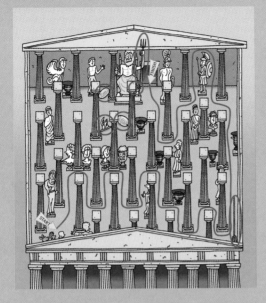

◀ Roman
Run
page 175

Into the ▶
Labyrinth
page 173

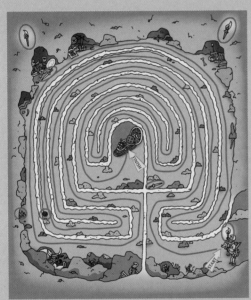

◀ The Silk
Road
page 176

On the ▶
March!
page 174

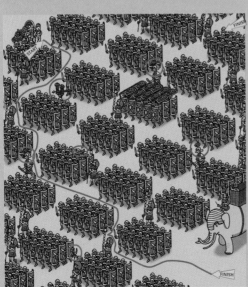

◀ Boom!
page 177

Viking ▶
Raid
page 179

◀ Art
Attack
page 182

Charge! ▶
page 180

◀ Sent to the
Tower
page 183

Fortress ▶
City
page 181

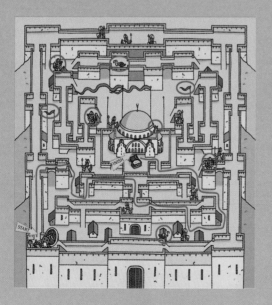

◀ Lance-A-Lot
page 184

Hampton ▶
Court Maze
page 185

◀ The Ball
Game
page 189

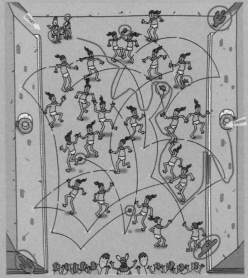

Big Heads ▶
page 187

◀ The Great
Plains
page 190

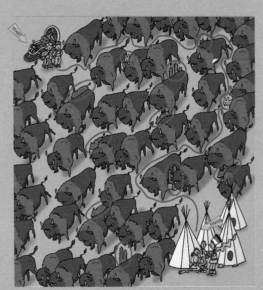

City of the ▶
Aztecs
page 188

◀ Totem
Poles
page 191

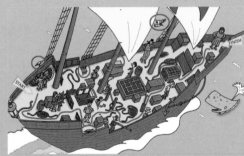

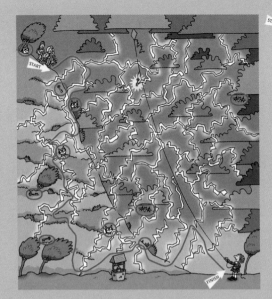

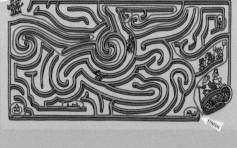

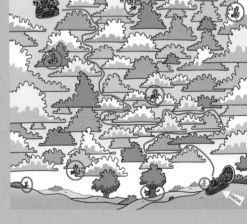

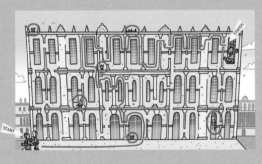

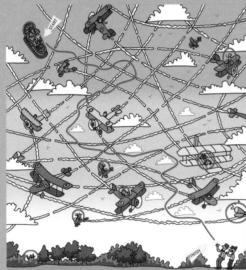